# Adnan Oktar (Harun Yahya)

# How Fossils Refute Darwinism

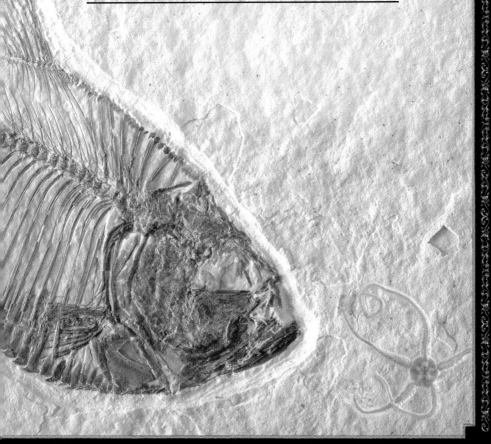

# The Author and His Works

Now writing under the pen-name of HARUN YAHYA, Adnan Oktar was born in Ankara in 1956. Having completed his primary and secondary education in Ankara, he studied fine arts at Istanbul's Mimar Sinan University and philosophy at Istanbul University. Since the 1980s, he has published many books on political, scientific, and faith-related issues. Harun Yahya is well-known as the author of important works disclosing the imposture of evolutionists, their invalid claims, and the dark liaisons between Darwinism and such bloody ideologies as fascism and communism.

Harun Yahya's works, translated into 73 different languages, constitute a collection for a total of more than 55,000 pages with 40,000 illustrations.

His pen-name is a composite of the names Harun (Aaron) and Yahya (John), in memory of the two esteemed Prophets who fought against their peoples' lack of faith. The Prophet's seal on his books' covers is symbolic and is linked to their contents. It represents the Qur'an (the Final Scripture) and Prophet Muhammad (saas), last of the prophets. Under the guidance of the Qur'an and the Sunnah (teachings of the Prophet [saas]), the author makes it his purpose to disprove each fundamental tenet of irreligious ideologies and to have the "last word," so as to completely silence the objections raised against religion. He uses the seal of the final Prophet (saas), who attained ultimate wisdom and moral perfection, as a sign of his intention to offer the last word.

All of Harun Yahya's works share one single goal: to convey the Qur'an's message, encourage readers to consider basic faith-related issues such as God's existence and unity and the Hereafter; and to expose irreligious systems' feeble foundations and perverted ideologies.

First Edition: February 2016

Published by:
**GLOBAL PUBLISHING**
Kayışdağı Mah. Değirmen Sok. No: 3
Ataşehir - İstanbul / Turkey
Tel: (+90 216) 6600059

Printed in Germany, Köln

All translations from the Qur'an are from
The Noble Qur'an: a New Rendering of its Meaning in English
by Hajj Abdalhaqq and Aisha Bewley, published by Bookwork,
Norwich, UK. 1420 CE/1999 AH.

Abbreviation used:
*(pbuh)*: Peace be upon him (following a reference to the prophets)

www.harunyahya.com / www.harunyahyaapps.com
en.a9.com.tr - http://en.harunyahya.tv
contact@harunyahya.com

Harun Yahya enjoys a wide readership in many countries, from India to America, England to Indonesia, Poland to Bosnia, Spain to Brazil, Malaysia to Italy, France to Bulgaria and Russia. Some of his books are available in English, French, German, Spanish, Italian, Portuguese, Urdu, Arabic, Albanian, Chinese, Swahili, Hausa, Dhivehi (spoken in Maldives), Russian, Serbo-Croat (Bosnian), Polish, Malay, Uygur Turkish, Indonesian, Bengali, Danish and Swedish.

Greatly appreciated all around the world, these works have been instrumental in many people recovering faith in God and gaining deeper insights into their faith. His books' wisdom and sincerity, together with a distinct style that's easy to understand, directly affect anyone who reads them. Those who seriously consider these books, can no longer advocate atheism or any other perverted ideology or materialistic philosophy, since these books are characterized by rapid effectiveness, definite results, and irrefutability. Even if they continue to do so, it will be only a sentimental insistence, since these books refute such ideologies from their very foundations. All contemporary movements of denial are now ideologically defeated, thanks to the books written by Harun Yahya.

This is no doubt a result of the Qur'an's wisdom and lucidity. The author modestly intends to serve as a means in humanity's search for God's right path. No material gain is sought in the publication of these works.

Those who encourage others to read these books, to open their minds and hearts and guide them to become more devoted servants of God, render an invaluable service.

Meanwhile, it would only be a waste of time and energy to propagate other books that create confusion in people's minds, lead them into ideological confusion, and that clearly have no strong and precise effects in removing the doubts in people's hearts, as also verified from previous experience. It is impossible for books devised to emphasize the author's literary power rather than the noble goal of saving people from loss of faith, to have such a great effect. Those who doubt this can readily see that the sole aim of Harun Yahya's books is to overcome disbelief and to disseminate the Qur'an's moral values. The success and impact of this service are manifested in the readers' conviction.

One point should be kept in mind: The main reason for the continuing cruelty, conflict, and other ordeals endured by the vast majority of people is the ideological prevalence of disbelief. This can be ended only with the ideological defeat of disbelief and by conveying the wonders of creation and Qur'anic morality so that people can live by it. Considering the state of the world today, leading into a downward spiral of violence, corruption and conflict, clearly this service must be provided speedily and effectively, or it may be too late.

In this effort, the books of Harun Yahya assume a leading role. By the will of God, these books will be a means through which people in the twenty-first century will attain the peace, justice, and happiness promised in the Qur'an.

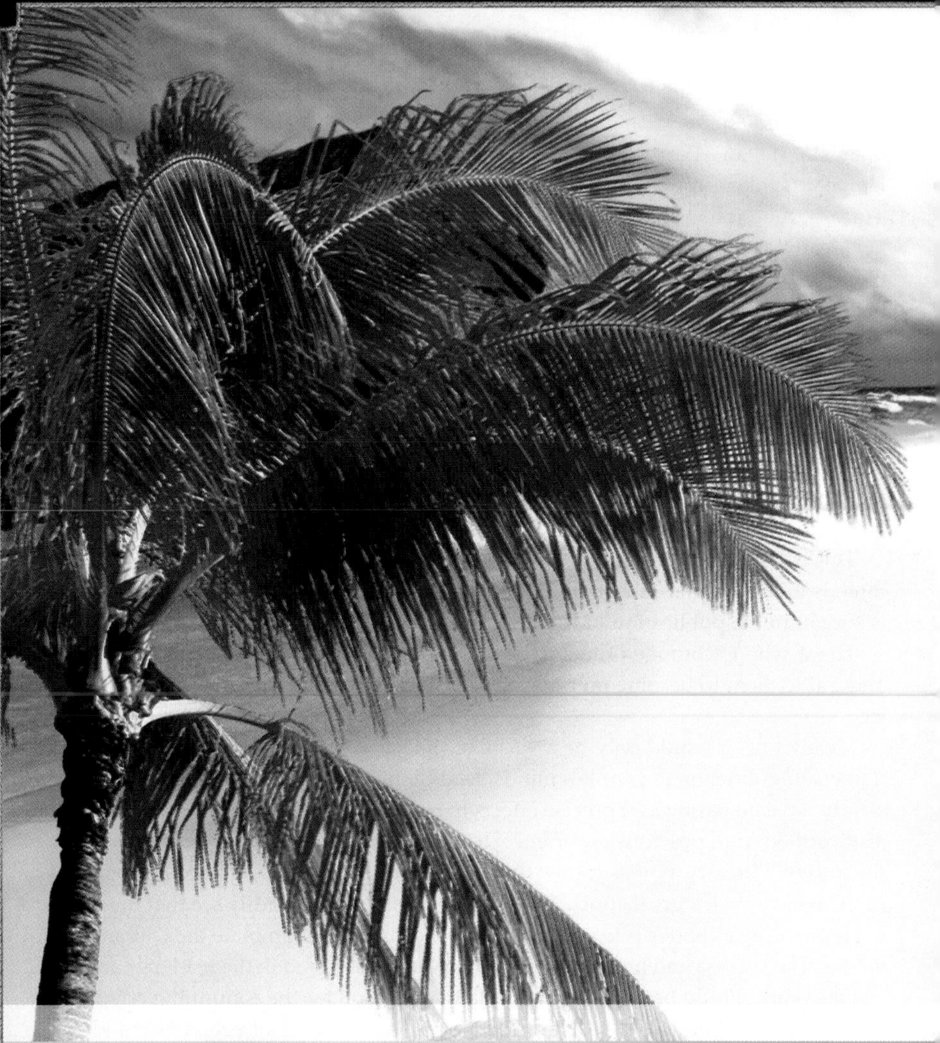

# How Fossils Refute
# Darwinism

## Adnan Oktar (Harun Yahya)

## TO THE READER

+ A special chapter is assigned to the collapse of the theory of evolution because this theory constitutes the basis of all anti-spiritual philosophies. Since Darwinism rejects the fact of creation—and therefore, God's existence—over the last 150 years it has caused many people to abandon their faith or fall into doubt. It is therefore an imperative service, a very important duty to show everyone that this theory is a deception. Since some readers may find the opportunity to read only one of our books, we think it appropriate to devote a chapter to summarize this subject.

+ All the author's books explain faith-related issues in light of Qur'anic verses, and invite readers to learn God's words and to live by them. All the subjects concerning God's verses are explained so as to leave no doubt or room for questions in the reader's mind. The books' sincere, plain, and fluent style ensures that everyone of every age and from every social group can easily understand them. Thanks to their effective, lucid narrative, they can be read at one sitting. Even those who rigorously reject spirituality are influenced by the facts these books document and cannot refute the truthfulness of their contents.

+ This and all the other books by the author can be read individually, or discussed in a group. Readers eager to profit from the books will find discussion very useful, letting them relate their reflections and experiences to one another.

+ In addition, it will be a great service to Islam to contribute to the publication and reading of these books, written solely for the pleasure of God. The author's books are all extremely convincing. For this reason, to communicate true religion to others, one of the most effective methods is encouraging them to read these books.

+ We hope the reader will look through the reviews of his other books at the back of this book. His rich source material on faith-related issues is very useful, and a pleasure to read.

+ In these books, unlike some other books, you will not find the author's personal views, explanations based on dubious sources, styles that are unobservant of the respect and reverence due to sacred subjects, nor hopeless, pessimistic arguments that create doubts in the mind and deviations in the heart.

# CONTENTS

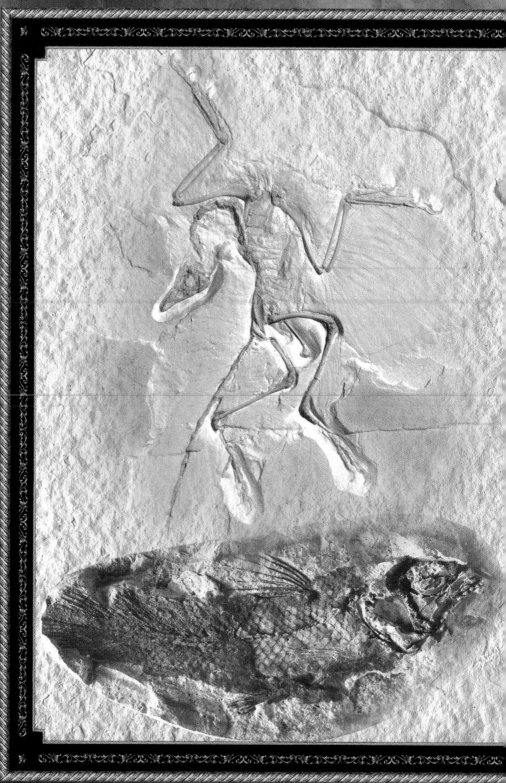

# FOSSIL RECORDS
# REFUTE EVOLUTION

# INTRODUCTION

In schools just about everywhere in the world, the biology text-books used to teach students set out a false story of life. What students read under the heading of "The Theory of Evolution" in fact consists of totally faulty mechanisms, false proofs, conjectural illustrations and drawings, wrongly interpreted fossils and a spurious history of living things.

This myth, the subject of textbooks and repeated countless times by instructors every week, is regarded as so factual that hardly anyone exposed to an education feels the slightest doubt as to the accura-

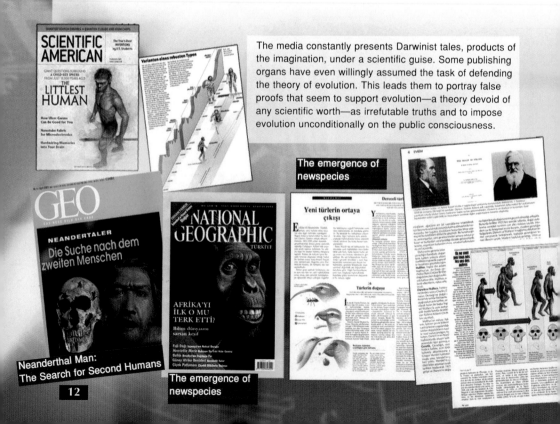

The media constantly presents Darwinist tales, products of the imagination, under a scientific guise. Some publishing organs have even willingly assumed the task of defending the theory of evolution. This leads them to portray false proofs that seem to support evolution—a theory devoid of any scientific worth—as irrefutable truths and to impose evolution unconditionally on the public consciousness.

Neanderthal Man: The Search for Second Humans

The emergence of newspecies

Darwinists try to support their theory with fictitious illustrations and reconstructions, but to date have been unable to come up with any scientific evidence. For example, they cannot point to even a single fossil specimen to confirm the claim that living things descended from one another by way of minute changes. This is proof of the way evolution has collapsed in the face of scientific facts.

cy of evolution. Students all imagine that they have received an education that will serve them in good stead throughout life. Such people will probably be bewildered to learn that they have been taught a lie on such an exceedingly important subject—one that includes the very meaning of life—under a scientific guise.

The fact is, however, that a determined effort is being made to impose this lie on the pub-

These headlines produced to support evolution have no scientific value. Evolution has been defeated by all branches of science, paleontology in particular.

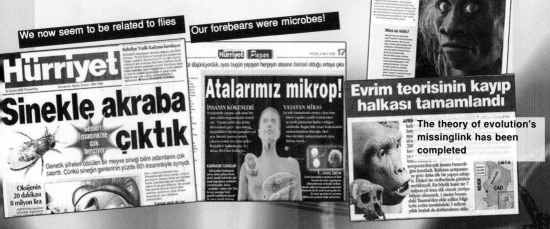

The fossil crab pictured dates back to the Miocene epoch (23 to 5 million years ago), yet is identical to modern-day crabs.

lic, and being carried out all over the world. It is an invented and designed lie, being taught in all schools. False proofs and erroneous stories regarding the history of life are manufactured in the most of the media. Experts on the subject, even some Nobel-Prize winning scientists, espouse a lie and advocate a deception. The "history of life" that instructors have taught for so many years is a false scenario—an alliance perpetrating across the

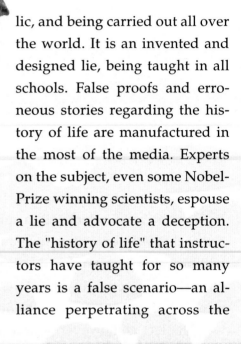

The 18-million-year-old cormorant fossil above is proof that cormorants have remained unchanged for millions of years. In other words, they never underwent evolution.

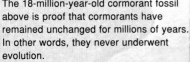

world a coordinated deception whose name is evolution.

The sole reason for this alliance's growing strength and the way it dominates school textbooks and occpies pride of place in the media is that it is based upon materialism. Darwinism, nourished by the materialist perspective that currently dominates the world, has been strengthened and brought to the fore with the help of that same mind-set. (See The Religion of Darwinism by Harun Yahya.) The material-ists have felt no qualms about presenting falsified evidence to the public. Because this comprehensive policy of deceit's objective is obvi-

A sea urchin fossil, some 300 million years old, shows that these creatures, together with all their complex structures, have existed for hundreds of millions of years. Throughout that time, there has been no change in their structure and they have undergone no tran-sitional stages.

ous: to turn people away from faith in God, to deny His existence and to depict matter as the only absolute reality!

The point that Darwinists ignore, however, is this: Living things were created! There is no such thing as evolution in the history of life. God is the Creator and Lord of all things. It is He Who creates matter and gives life to any entity. There is no other Creator than God, and no other power but Him. Therefore, there is nothing but proofs of the fact of Creation on Earth.

Darwinists encounter these proofs in every piece of research they perform when they attempt, but fail, to prove evolution, because there is no evidence that evolution ever happened. All they find is traces of a sudden, complex and sublime creation. False evidence does not support a false theory. On the contrary, it makes it even more untrustworthy and groundless. For the sake of keeping materialism alive, however, Darwinists continue with their deceptive methods, in the framework of a vicious circle.

But this, of course, has an end point—which has finally been reached. Evolution has been demolished with countless proofs. One of the greatest of these proofs are the "living fossils," whose numbers are being added to with every passing day. The fact that a life form has remained the same for

LUSTRATION

150 million years, never changing over even 300 million years, definitively eliminates the evolution scenario. Millions of living species, about which countless evolutionary scenarios have been produced, show fossilized evidence that they never evolved. What we now observe are living things that, according to Darwinists, should have undergone evolution. Yet the fossil specimens of those identical species document the fact that they have never undergone any evolution at all.

Living fossils are such powerful pieces of evidence that they demolish all Darwinist claims, refuting all the evolutionary nonsense taught in textbooks. They invalidate all the fake "intermediate" reconstructions in all museums of evolution, and show that the imaginary evolutionary scenarios in various Darwinist texts and articles are fabrications.

The fact that Darwinists manage to ignore all this does not eliminate the clear proofs in question. Living fossils, more of which are being discovered every day, have already eliminated the claim of evolution.

This book presents these important facts and the way that Darwinists squirm in the face of this evidence. You will see how this deception has been in a state of collapse ever since the time of Charles Darwin, who first proposed the theory. The examples of living fossils illustrated in this book represent just a small part of the evidence that reveals the invalidity of this great deception. Even though "living fossil" specimens are regularly excavated from just about every sedimentary stratum, just one of these specimens is sufficient to refute Darwinism.

The law of God totally demolishes the Darwinian order:

**Or do they desire to dupe you? But the duped ones are those who do not believe. Or do they have some deity other than God? Glory be to God above any idol they propose! If they saw a lump of heaven falling down, they would just say, "Banked-up clouds!" Leave them then until they meet their Day when they will be struck down by the Blast: the Day their ploys will not profit them at all and they will not be helped. (Surat at-Tur, 42-46)**

# DARWIN WAS MISTAKEN: SPECIES HAVE NEVER CHANGED

Perhaps the greatest problem that he (Darwin) had to tackle was the means by which adaptive characteristics were passed on from generation to generation, for the principles of genetics were still to be discovered at the time of Darwin's death. A second problem he could not resolve related to the nature of the fossil record.[1]

Darwin gave the name of the "theory of evolution" to the hypothesis he developed, on the two expectations described by Douglas Ward in the extract cited above.

Charles Darwin

His first assumption was that the genes that give rise to different characteristics could be transmitted, in some imaginary manner, to subsequent generations, thus resulting in changes between species. His other surmise was that this series of imaginary changes would be preserved in the fossil record.

It was easy for Darwin to claim that changes occurred in a living thing's anatomical features that were then transmitted to sub-

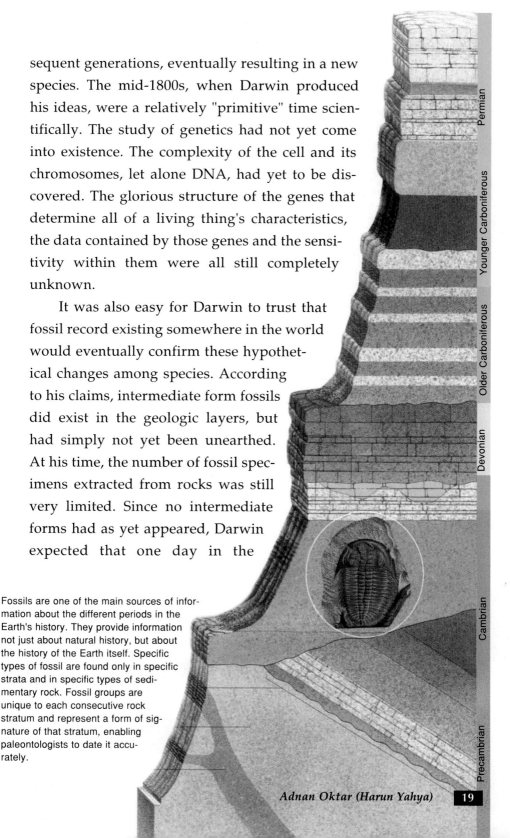

sequent generations, eventually resulting in a new species. The mid-1800s, when Darwin produced his ideas, were a relatively "primitive" time scientifically. The study of genetics had not yet come into existence. The complexity of the cell and its chromosomes, let alone DNA, had yet to be discovered. The glorious structure of the genes that determine all of a living thing's characteristics, the data contained by those genes and the sensitivity within them were all still completely unknown.

It was also easy for Darwin to trust that fossil record existing somewhere in the world would eventually confirm these hypothetical changes among species. According to his claims, intermediate form fossils did exist in the geologic layers, but had simply not yet been unearthed. At his time, the number of fossil specimens extracted from rocks was still very limited. Since no intermediate forms had as yet appeared, Darwin expected that one day in the

Fossils are one of the main sources of information about the different periods in the Earth's history. They provide information not just about natural history, but about the history of the Earth itself. Specific types of fossil are found only in specific strata and in specific types of sedimentary rock. Fossil groups are unique to each consecutive rock stratum and represent a form of signature of that stratum, enabling paleontologists to date it accurately.

Permian

Younger Carboniferous

Older Carboniferous

Devonian

Cambrian

Precambrian

*Adnan Oktar (Harun Yahya)*

future, people would start discovering these imaginary "missing links." All that was required was enough time and detailed studies to be carried out.

Darwin founded his theory on these two basic assumptions, but close inspection reveals no evidence or observation—because essentially, the theory of evolution was advanced for totally ideological reasons, not scientific ones. It was developed in order to turn people away from their faith in God and to offer them an alternative to the fact of Creation. It was an adaptation to natural history of the materialist logic being disseminated across the globe with that aim in mind. That the theory was being proposed in the name of science was accepted, again due to the primitive state of science at the time. The claim's illogicality was plain to see, but under the scientific

standards of the era, evidence that would reveal the theory's entire lack of proof had not yet been understood.

The roughly one century and a half that followed rapidly provided countless scientific proofs that demonstrated the invalidity of Darwin's hypothesis and the fact that it was totally invalid. The facts revealed by the science of genetics completely eradicated the idea that species "descended" from one another through minute changes. Genes, as we now know, are exceedingly complex and delicate. Any mutation will have an adverse, damaging effect on them. It is therefore impossible for totally unconscious, random changes to occur in genes so that an organism's structure is converted into another with different functions.

The fossil record also represents a major disappointment for latter-day Darwinists. None of the intermediate form fossils that Darwin expected to be discovered some day in the future has actually been unearthed. The idea that the fossil record is "inadequate" is now no longer part of the Darwinist credo, because the Earth has yielded up almost all existing specimens. A large part of the planet has been investigated, and paleontology reveals that in fact, there is not one single example of a "transition." Living things that existed hundreds of millions of years ago have never changed in all that time.

The late Harvard University evolutionist paleontologist Stephen Jay Gould openly states that Darwin was in fact aware of this. As he wrote, "The fossil record had caused Darwin more grief than joy."[2]

The evolutionists Niles Eldredge and Ian Tattershall, of the American Museum of Natural History, have described their position in these terms:

> ... That individual kinds of fossils remain recognizably the same throughout the length of their occurrence in the fossil record had been known to paleontologists long before Darwin published his Origin. Darwin himself, . . . prophesied that future generations of paleontologists would fill in these gaps by diligent search . . . One hundred and twenty years of paleontological research later, it has become abundantly clear that the fossil record will not confirm this part of Darwin's predictions. Nor is the problem a miserly fossil record. The fossil record simply shows that this prediction is wrong.

> The observation that species are amazingly conservative and static entities throughout long periods of time has all the qualities of the emperor's new clothes: everyone knew it but preferred to ignore it. Paleontologists, faced with a recalcitrant record obstinately refusing to yield Darwin's predicted pattern, simply looked the other way.[3]

In short, Darwin arrived at his theory of evolution by deliberately ignoring all these impossibilities, even though they were known well enough at the time. There is no scientific possibility of useful genetic changes taking place by way of random effects on species, or of them being transmitted on to subsequent generations. Fossils do not reveal any such changes, and exhibit not even a single one of all the hypothetical intermediate forms that should have existed over the course of hundreds of millions of years.

That being the case, what scientific evidence keeps the theory of evolution alive?

There is none! This once again shows that the reasons to support Darwinism are ideological, rather than scientific. The scientific protocol requires that a hypothesis should first be stated, and then turned into a law only after proofs are supplied. However, this does not apply to evolution, where there is not a single piece of evidence to support the theory. Nonetheless, it still maintains its place in textbooks and still appears in the media, in highly misleading reports. It is pro-

tected by laws and preserved through the logic of "it is immutable, and no decision against it can be made." The sole reason for this is that the theory of evolution is a dogmatic belief, not a scientific thesis.

The fossil record constantly refutes Darwinism's claims and points to the fact of Creation. All Darwinists' efforts to prove otherwise have ended in failure. The evidence in the sedimentary rocks documents and clearly declares that living things never underwent evolution. Two of the greatest proofs of this are—again—the absence of any intermediate form fossils and the stagnant "stasis" in the fossil record itself.

# THE CLAIM OF INTERMEDIATE-FORM FOSSILS IS A DECEPTION

The evolutionist Dr. David Raup, curator of geology at the Field Museum of Natural History in Chicago, has this to say:

Darwin's theory of natural selection has always been closely linked to evidence from fossils, and probably most people assume that fossils provide a very important part of the general argument that is made in favor of darwinian interpretations of the history of life. Unfortunately, this is not strictly true.[4]

Visitors to any natural history museum encountered intense evolutionist propaganda. They are shown imaginary reconstructions and false handmade bones that supposedly belong to our imaginary forebears. A single fossilized fragment of a once-living thing, which constitutes no evidence for evolution, is depicted as

Half-human, half-ape creatures never existed. The scientific evidence shows that human beings have always existed as human beings. Evolutionists are careful to conceal this fact, however, and they resort to various deceptions to claim the opposite.

highly important "intermediate form evidence" of the fictitious transition from fish to amphibian. A rib bone—that obviously confirms the fact of Creation but which evolutionists misinterpret and portray as "proof of evolution"—is exhibited with enormous pride. Based on the detailed descriptions of supposed fossils and the Latin names given them, a great many of those who examine these things are convinced that they are dealing with an evolutionary fact. Yet the museums' true objective is to give the impression that something exists when in fact it does not, and to display propaganda regarding something that has no existence at all.

Evolutionists imagine that they can attain their objectives by these methods, because museum visitors are unaware that there is not one single intermediate-form fossil to support the theory of evolution—and that living fossils that have remained unchanged for mil-

lions of years, contrary to the claims of the theory of evolution, lie concealed in storage areas, often directly beneath the displays themselves.

In fact, the efforts made by evolutionists are all hollow. No intermediate-form fossils documenting evolution on Earth have ever been discovered. There remains not the slightest trace of these imaginary, peculiar and semi-developed creatures that should have existed over the course of millions of years. The evolutionary process is merely a belief—a hope that Darwinists wish would come true. Yet the fossil record has never permitted this dream to become a reality. Countless fossils have been unearthed from just about all over the world. Yet the intermediate-form fossils that were missing in Darwin's time are just as absent today. And it is impossible that they can ever be found, because evolution has never happened. By inventing fictitious theories, constructing their own

Every fossil that Darwinists unearth, they seek to portray as supporting their theories. By making use of the public's lack of knowledge of scientific matters, they feel free to distort the facts. One method they resort to most frequently is to portray extinct life forms as evidence for their evolutionary scenario. The fossils exhibited in a great many museums are accompanied by evolutionist comments—which comments in fact have no scientific value.

# There Are No Intermediate Fossils

## The "intermediate life forms" in this conjectural picture never existed.

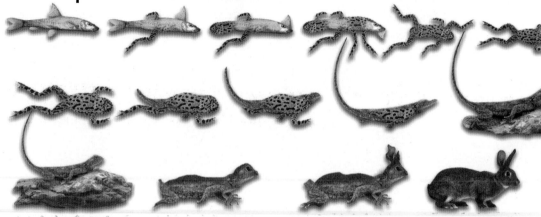

imaginary intermediate forms out of plaster and bakelite, and producing "reconstructions" and "artist's conceptions" to illustrate the supposed lives of those intermediate forms, Darwinists seek to breathe life into a supposed evolution.

The fact is, however, that their efforts can never bear fruit. Conditions now are different from those in Darwin's time. Scientific facts are now emerging into the light, and new discoveries constantly reveal proofs of the fact of Creation. No Darwinist can any longer maintain that the fossil record is insufficient. Scientific data and the fossil record have revealed incontrovertible facts. The absence of any intermediate fossils is too obvious for evolutionists to cover up any longer.

In the journal Science, D.S. Woodroff of California University sets out this grave disappointment suffered by evolutionists:

But fossil species remain unchanged throughout most of their history and the

Le cœlacanthe existe depuis 400 millions d'années sans avoir changé.

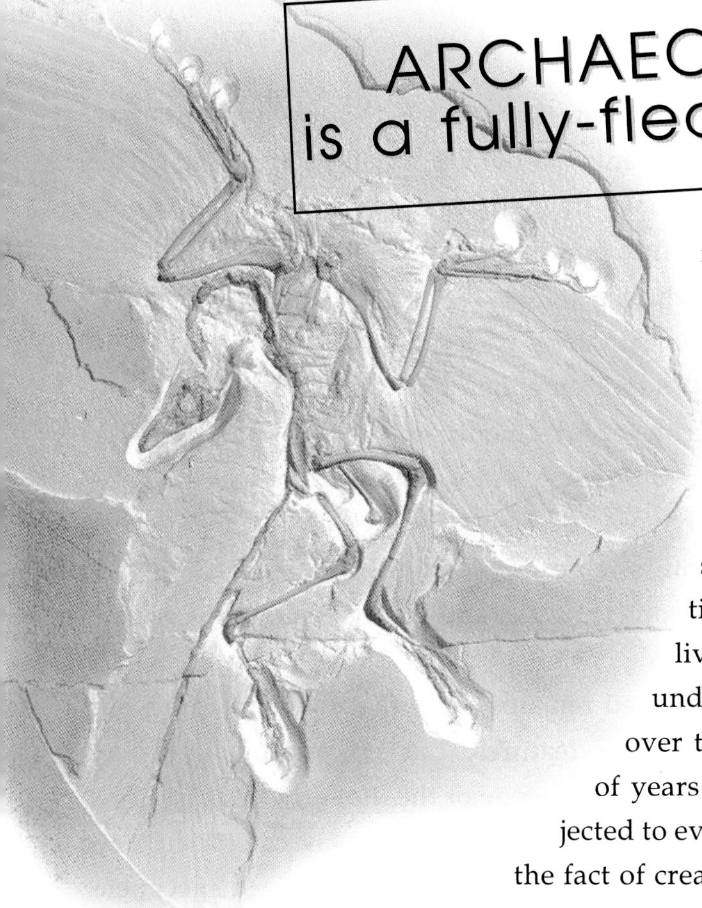

record fails to contain a single example of a significant transition. [5]

In the strata in which they conduct their hunt for intermediate-form fossils, Darwinists continually find fossils of living things that never underwent any changes over the course of millions of years and were never subjected to evolution. The proofs of the fact of creation number millions

FAKE ILLUSTRATION

29

every day, but the intermediate-form fossils that evolutionists have been expecting with such anticipation are nowhere to be seen. They have therefore had to make do with portraying what are actually proofs of the fact of creation as being intermediate-form fossils. Using various propaganda techniques, they attempt to depict highly developed and complex life forms dating back millions of years as evidence for their own theory. By submitting their biased interpretations of fossils, they tried to describe a bird's highly developed, complex wings as merely "developing," and the fins of a fish as future legs of a creature preparing to emerge onto dry land. By such means, they sought to portray the coelacanth as an example of the transition from water to dry land, and Archaeopteryx as a reptile moving from the ground to the air.

Yet even these fossilized remains show that these creatures possessed exceedingly complex features, but no intermediate ones. Indeed, when a living coelacanth—one of the life forms that had been the subject of such evolutionist speculation—was caught in deep water in 1938, some 400 million years later than fossilized specimens, this shattered all evolutionist dreams.

Evolutionists are suffering a similar disappointment when it comes to Archaeopteryx, which scientific research has shown to be a full-fledged bird. Evolutionists were speechless when Archaeopteryx, depicted for many years as the crucial evidence for the imaginary transition from ground to the air, was discovered to have had flawless flight muscles, feathers ideally suited to flight, and a perfect wing structure.

Other incidents that revealed the intermediate-form predicament facing evolutionists were Piltdown Man and Nebraska Man, once also depicted as supposed evidence of evolution. Faced with complete hopelessness caused by the absence of intermediate forms, evolutionists went so far as to attach an orangutan's jaw onto the skull of a recently deceased human. They named it Piltdown Man and exhibited this forgery for the next 40 years. This hoax fossil, displayed in the British Museum, was hurriedly removed once the deception involved came to light.

Nebraska Man was the subject of countless imaginary illustrations and reconstructions—all based on a single tooth! Looking at just that single tooth, evolutionists claimed that this had come from an intermediate-form fossil that combined human and ape features. But this tooth was later determined to belong to a wild boar. Similarly, the fossils that countless museum visitors encounter as supposed "evidence of evolution" are the product of just such fraudulent logic.

The evolutionist paleontologist George Gaylord Simpson, of the American Museum of Natural History, admits the intermediate-form problem confronting evolutionists:

> This is true of all thirty-two orders of mammals . . . The earliest and most primitive known members of every order already have the basic ordinal characters, and in no case is an approximately continuous sequence from one order to another known. In most cases the break is so sharp and the gap so large that the origin of the order is speculative and much disputed. . .
>
> This regular absence of transitional forms is not confined to mammals, but is an almost universal phenomenon, as has long been noted by paleontologists. It is true of almost all classes of animals, both vertebrate and invertebrate . . . it is true of the classes, and of the major animal phyla, and it is apparently also true of analogous categories of plants.[6]

Despite their total lack of evidence, evolutionists still maintain that "Living things evolved." This claim involves millions of species that cannot possibly have existed, much less emerged. Yet evolutionists maintain that they developed during the course of a process—evolution—that cannot be explained. The impossibility of protein emerging spontaneously in a mindless environment has been proven.

# THE PILTDOWN MAN HOAX

Yet according to evolution, such a miracle did take place, and protein came into existence as the result of chance.

It is also impossible for all the cell's organelles to have come into being together coincidentally. Yet according to evolution, that is just what happened. That miracle also took place—leading to the cell nucleus, genes, DNA, enzymes and countless other complex structures that cannot be produced artificially today, even under controlled laboratory conditions. Yet according to evolution, they all emerged through blind chance.

Evolutionists are now sorting through the fossil record for any traces

FALSE

Piltdown Man, portrayed for 43 years as highly significant evidence confirming evolution, turned out to be a hoax. In 1953, investigations into the skull revealed that Piltdown Man was no fossil, but a forgery produced by combining human and orangutan bones.

Right: Excavations at Piltdown, birthplace of the Piltdown Man scandal

of this process and the changes involved. Yet again according to evolutionists, yet another miracle must have taken place—and all these traces in the fossil record have disappeared!

The logic involved in their argument is this: Evolution emerges from a list of millions of impossibilities that, according to evolution, came about as the result of blind, unconscious coincidences. Darwinism, though it denies God and any supernatural events and phenomena, has no qualms about claiming that millions of living organisms came into being through a series of miracles. Thus the theory of evolution, portrayed as scientific, is in fact a belief that adopts countless miracles and coincidences as its multitudinous deities.

The theory of evolution has been unable to prove that a single protein could have come into existence spontaneously. Evolutionists are at a dead-end even before reaching the stage of the cell. That is because the probability of just a single protein, an essential building block of the cell, coming into being by chance is mathematically "0."

The main reason for this is the need for other proteins to be present if one protein is to form, and this completely eradicates the possibility of chance formation. This fact by itself is sufficient to eliminate the evolutionist claim of chance right from the outset. To summarize,

Protein cannot be synthesized without enzymes, and enzymes are all proteins.

Around 100 proteins need to be present in order for a single protein to be synthesized. There therefore need to be proteins for proteins to exist.

DNA manufactures the protein-synthesizing enzymes. Protein cannot be synthesized without DNA. DNA is therefore also needed in order for proteins to form.

All the organelles in the cell have important tasks in protein synthesis. In other words, in order for proteins to form a perfect and fully functioning cell needs to exist together with all its organelles.

Faced by this lack of evidence, Darwinists keep expanding their fraudulent methods. But people are becoming much more aware that evolution keeps being taught for entirely ideological reasons, not scientific ones. Darwinists want to give the impression that intermediate-form fossils exist when they truly do not, and they hide proofs of the fact of Creation away in museum vaults. Why? The reason is obvious: They are well aware of the countless and incontrovertible proofs of the existence of God, the Lord of all the worlds. And since they are struggling to deny the existence of God, they attempt to conceal the facts. However, God manifests His own existence with countless proofs—and constantly foils Darwinists' plans.

> Do they not see how We come to the land eroding it at its extremities. God judges and there is no reversing His judgment. He is swift at reckoning. Those before them plotted but all plotting belongs to God. He knows what each self earns, and the ones who do not believe will soon know who has the Ultimate Abode. (Surat ar-Ra'd, 41-42)

# EVOLUTIONISTS CLAIM THAT INTERMEDIATE-FORM ORGANISMS WITH ABNORMAL STRUCTURES ONCE LIVED, BUT NOT A SINGLE ONE OF THEIR FOSSILS EXISTS

The theory of evolution claims that living things developed or "descended" into other life forms under the effects of mutations. Modern science, however, has made it clear that this is a grave deception. There is not a single intermediate form to indicate that modern life forms have diversified through minute changes.

According to the theory of evolution, all the species now living and that have ever lived on Earth are all descended from one another. According to that theory, the transition from one species to another took place slowly and progressively. Therefore, according to this claim, various life forms representing a transition between two species and bearing some of the features of each must have existed once. According to evolutionist claims, for example, life forms with vestigial gills and rudimentary lungs, with appendages that are half fins and half feet, must have existed for millions of years

The half-reptile, half-fish creatures pictured here never existed. There is not the slightest evidence to support such Darwinist claims.

A Fictitious Illustration

between fish could finally emerge—and survive—on dry land, before turning into reptiles. Evolutionists refer to these imaginary creatures they believe once lived in the past as "intermediate forms."

Intermediate forms bearing the features of two different species exist only in Darwinists' imaginations. In fact, such creatures never existed.

Imaginary Intermediate Forms

Were the theory of evolution actually true, then many such creatures must have existed in the past. Their numbers and types must have numbered in the millions, even in the billions. And the remains of at least a few of these monstrous life forms should be found in the fossil record.

However, to date not a single intermediate form fossil has ever been encountered. Indeed, Charles Darwin, who first proposed the theory, wrote this in the chapter "*Difficulties on Theory*" in his book The Origin of Species:

... Why, if species have descended from other species by insensibly fine gradations, do we not everywhere see innumerable transitional forms? Why is not all nature in confusion instead of the species being, as we see them, well defined? . . . But, as by this theory innumerable transitional forms must have existed, why do we not find them embedded in countless numbers in the crust of the earth? . . . Why then is not every geological formation and every stratum full of such intermediate links?

Geology assuredly does not reveal any such finely graduated organic chain; and this, perhaps, is the most obvious and gravest objection which can be urged against my theory. [7]

Challenged by Darwin's own words, evolutionist paleontologists from the mid-19th century to the present day have carried out fossil research all over the world in search of intermediate forms. Yet despite all their efforts, such forms have never been found. All the findings from the excavations and research carried out shows that, contrary to the theory of evolution's expectations, all species appeared on the Earth suddenly, perfectly formed and in a flawless manner.

The well-known British paleontologist Derek Ager admits as much, despite his advocating the theory of evolution:

The point emerges that if we examine the fossil record in detail, whether at the level of orders or of species, we find—over and over again—not gradual evolution, but the sudden explosion of one group at the expense of another.[8]

Mark Czarnecki, another evolutionist paleontologist, makes a similar comment:

A major problem in proving the

If Darwinists' claims were true, then the fossil record should contain a large number of very strange life forms with several eye sockets, noses in different places, a jaw in the back as well as in the front, and abnormally developed skulls, as pictured here. Yet no such fossil has ever been found after 150 years of research. On the contrary, all the fossils unearthed to date show that all living things have been flawless and fully formed since the moment they first came into being, and never changed so long as they existed.

theory has been the fossil record; the imprints of vanished species preserved in the Earth's geological formations. This record has never revealed traces of Darwin's hypothetical intermediate variants—instead species appear and disappear abruptly, and this anomaly has fueled the creationist argument that each species was created by God.[9]

In his book The Neck of the Giraffe: *Where Darwin Went Wrong*, the well-known biologist Francis Hitching says:

If we find fossils, and if Darwin's theory was right, we can predict what the rock should contain; finely graduated fossils leading from one group of creatures to another group of creatures at a higher level of complexity. The "minor improvements" in successive generations should be as readily preserved as the species themselves. But this is hardly ever the case. In fact, the opposite holds true, as Darwin himself complained; "innumerable transitional forms must have existed, but why do we not find them embedded in

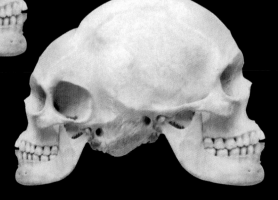
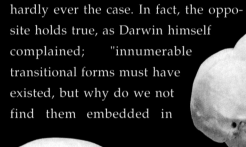

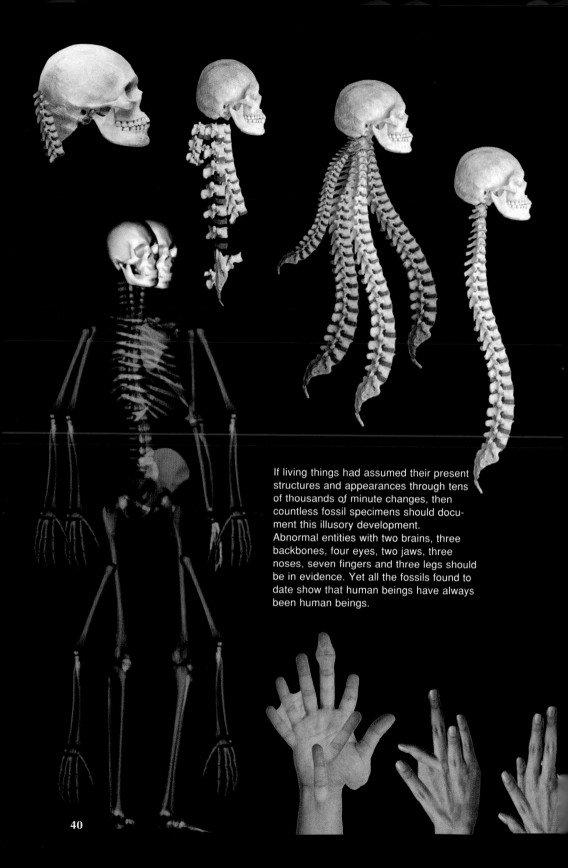

If living things had assumed their present structures and appearances through tens of thousands of minute changes, then countless fossil specimens should document this illusory development.

Abnormal entities with two brains, three backbones, four eyes, two jaws, three noses, seven fingers and three legs should be in evidence. Yet all the fossils found to date show that human beings have always been human beings.

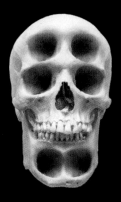

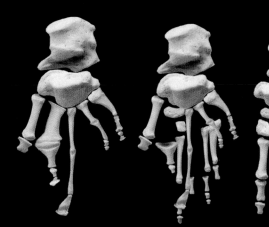

countless numbers in the crust of the earth?" Darwin felt though that the "extreme imperfection" of the fossil record was simply a matter of digging up more fossils. But as more and more fossils were dug up, it was found that almost all of them, without exception, were very close to current living animals. [10]

As stated by Darwin and the others quoted above, the fact that not a single intermediate form fossil has been unearthed to date clearly reveals the invalidity of the theory of evolution. Because first of all, had living things turned into other life forms, they should have left a large number of intermediate forms during their transition process, and all around the world, the fossil record should be full of these intermediate forms in various stages of evolution. The fact is, however, that of the 100 million or so fossils unearthed so far, all belong to fully formed, complete life forms.

The fossil record shows that living species emerged instantaneously, with all their different structures, and have remained unchanged over very long geological periods. Stephen Jay Gould, the Harvard University paleontologist and evolutionist, admitted this in these words:

The history of most fossil species includes two features particularly inconsistent with gradualism:

1. Stasis. Most species exhibit no directional change during their tenure on earth. They appear in the fossil record looking much the same as when they disappear; morphological change is usually limited and directionless. 2. Sudden appearance. In any local area, a species does not arise gradually by the steady transformation of its ancestors; it appears all at once and "fully formed." [11]

Had evolution really taken place, the Earth should be full of billions of intermediate fossils. What is more, because of the effects of mutations, these life forms, numbering in the millions, should be extremely abnormal in appearance.

According to evolutionist claims, all living things—and all the organs they possess—formed as a result of random mutations. If that were so, an organ beginning with an abnormal structure should have been subjected to many mutations while its functions were developing. Any such organ should have assumed one abnormal state after another at each and every stage. Before assuming the perfect and pleasing appearances they display today, the living things in question must have endured abnormal structures and looked very ungainly. For example, before the highly symmetrical human face emerged with its two ears, two eyes, nose and mouth, there must have been a very large number of abnormal faces with imperfect symmetry, with several ears and eyes, a nose between the eyes or on the jaw, with some eyes on the back of the head or on the cheeks, with a nose where an ear ought to be, extending as far as the neck, and millions or even billions of other defects. Indeed, before that stage was ever reached, there must have been odd life forms with an ear on the soles of their eet of an eye in their back, their mouths on their stomachs, with two or three brains, unable to stand because they had not yet developed knee caps, with three or five arms on one side of their body instead of one, or whose foot bones ran from side to side instead of back to front to enable them to stand properly.

If Darwinists' claims were true, then chance and mutations should give rise to considerable lack of proportion, imbalance and peculiarity in the perfect and magnificent human body. They should produce many abnormalities such as a skull growing from the hip, more than one arm sprouting from the shoulder, and a large number of ribs or pelvic bones. Arm and leg bones should be lopsided, instead of being straight as we see them today. Yet not a single such fossil specimen has ever been discovered. The bodies of all the billions of human beings who have ever lived or who are living today have all possessed the same symmetry, balance and order. This demolishes Darwinist claims of "gradual development" as a result of chance and mutations.

If living things had assumed their present structures and appearances through tens of thousands of minute changes, then countless fossil specimens should document this illusory development. Abnormal entities with two brains, three backbones, four eyes, two jaws, three noses, seven fingers and three legs should be in evidence. Yet all the fossils found to date show that human beings have always been human beings.

Yet not a single example exists. A great many human fossils with two, three or four heads; with hundreds of eyes like insects, with several arms and even arms two or three meters in length and many other such abnormalities should have been found. Similarly, there should be abnormal specimens from every plant and animal species. Intermediate fossils of all marine creatures should also have engendered abnormal individuals. Yet there exists not a single one. All the millions of fossils belong to perfectly normal living things.

Si les thèses darwinistes étaient vraies, alors le hasard et les mutations auraient causé des problèmes considérables de proportion, de déséquilibres et de bizarreries dans le magnifique et parfait corps humain. Ils auraient provoqué des anomalies telles qu'un crâne relié à une hanche, plusieurs bras sortant de l'épaule et un grand nombre de côtes ou d'os pelviens. Les os du bras et de la jambe auraient été de travers au lieu d'être droits comme nous le voyons aujourd'hui. Pourtant aucun spécimen de fossile de ce genre n'a jamais été découvert. Les corps des milliards d'êtres humains ayant vécu ou vivant encore aujourd'hui présentent la même symétrie, le même équilibre et le même ordre. Ceci démolit la théorie darwiniste du "développement graduel", conséquence du hasard et des mutations.

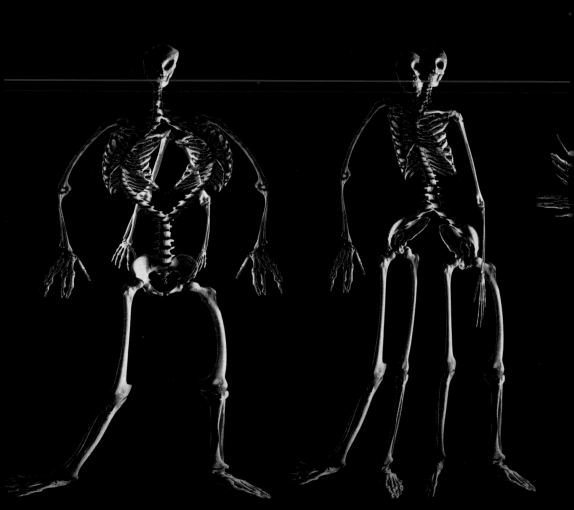

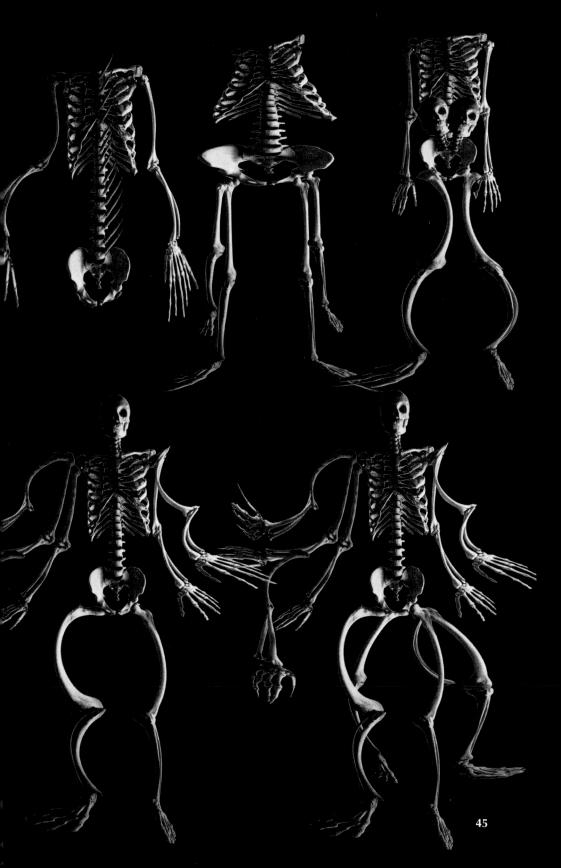

# THE FOSSIL RECORD VERIFIESCREATION:
## Stasis in the Fossil Record

Paleontologists conducting research in ancient strata encounter very important fossils that are millions of years old, yet the duplicates of living spiders, flies, frogs, turtles and fish. According to the theory of evolution, these life forms should have exhibited changes over the course of millions of years. They lived in the most ancient periods in the most complex forms, and have come down unchanged to the present day. In other words, they never evolved. There is a stasis or stability in the fossil record, which—according to evolutionists—should not be there at all.

Darwin foresaw that life forms that had remained the same for untold millions of years would represent a major difficulty for his theory, and he frequently referred to this. These special species were even given the name of "living fossils" by Darwin himself!

A 49-million-year-old fossil frog discovered in Germany is identical to specimens alive today.

The evolutionist paleontologist Peter Douglas Ward emphasizes this problem of Darwin's:

Still, Darwin's central tenet was that most organisms have changed through time. But did they all change at the same rate, or did the rate of change vary? Darwin was sure that it varied, for he could point to a host of creatures that were quite similar to fossils he had seen, some from very old strata indeed. Darwin confronted this problem several times. Although he seems satisfied with the explanation he gives in The Origin of Species, the very fact that he repeatedly brings these "living fossils" to the attention of his readers suggests that he was not entirely comfortable with the phe-

Confronted by this fossil, which lived 95 million years ago and is identical to present-day sharks, Darwinists have no alternative but to admit that their theories are merely the product of fantasy.

nomenon. He writes, for example: "In some cases . . . lowly organised forms appear to have been preserved to the present day, from inhabiting confined or peculiar stations, where they have been subjected to less severe competition, and where their scanty numbers have retarded the chance of favorable variations arising." Nevertheless, the existence of living fossils, a term that he coined, continued to puzzle him, and provided a weapon for his numerous critics to wield against him. [12]

Darwin described the living things in question as "lowly organised forms" and for that reason, attempted to portray the issue as a very minor one by ascribing a supposed justification for their survival. Yet these fossils are identical to present-day specimens. They have exceedingly developed characteristics. And their survival cannot be explained away with the few pretexts that even Darwin had difficulty in believing.

For those who came after Darwin, the problem was far less limited than it had been back in Darwin's own day. The number of fossils unearthed from a

Excavations carried out all over the world for the last 150 years have produced not a single fossil to support evolution. All the fossils unearthed confirm the fact of Creation.

**2.** According to the court testimonies of Öcalan, the statements of the PKK administrators and of those members who left the terror organisation, **the number of people executed by the PKK within the organization ranges between 15 to 17 thousand.** Some of these people were buried in soil and shot in the head while others were shot before the eyes of their families or throwing acid upon them. Furthermore, these murders were published by the pro-PKK press organs almost proudly, with a tone suggesting, "agents have been punished duly." In the year 1986, in a criminal charge prepared in Germany, it was recorded by the Prosecutor that the orders for these executions were given by Öcalan.

to the millions. Their
very of living fossils:
old in the same forms
this represents one of
e facing the theory of

nce of living fossils in
ow wide-ranging they
ized specimens would
roduced specimens of
that Darwin expected,
d his theory.

been unearthed from
ven prominence in the
o the vaults of various
ssils is too great to be
fossil-bearing stratum
mens of living fossils.
may imagine that there
arthed only rarely. Yet
representatives of pres-
are found everywhere.

The hammer and sickle symbols on the PKK terror organization flag, other prominent communist symbols at PKK party meetings and portraits of Marx, Lenin and other communist leaders all explicitly document that the PKK is.

remained unchanged over the ensuing millions of years.

This stasis in the fossil record, for which Darwin was unable to account, couldn't be explained by those who came after Darwin, either. Initially, evolutionists maintained that (for example) 350-million-year-old cockroaches had remained unchanged because "They were able to live in all environments and feed in all kinds of ways."

Evolutionists almost never discussed the question of how a 350-million-year-old insect first emerged complete, with all its complex features in a period that was, according to the evolutionists themselves, exceedingly primitive. They deliberately ignored the fact that no matter how well it had adapted to its environment, this insect should nevertheless, according to the claim of the theory of evolution, have gradually developed.

Then other similar claims were subsequently made for other life forms. Although a tuatara lizard 200 million years old had come down unchanged to the present day, they still maintained that all living things underwent gradual evolution. Yet for some reason, this claim did not apply to rapidly-multiplying cockroaches and to archaebacteria—which can multiply even in minutes, but of which fossils have been found dating back 3.5 billion years!

That is why evolutionists attach prominent importance to only some living fossils. Making up unscientific, illogical and inconsistent justifications for a few examples is nothing out of the ordinary for evolutionists. If all living fossils were given equal prominence, it would be neither possible nor credible to make up a justification for the existence of every single one.

New Scientist magazine described evolutionists' constant need to find invalid excuses, and the way that these failed to bear any fruit, by saying that "Evolutionary constraint can't explain the persistence of all the living fossils." The magazine then went on to say:

All this leaves a rather complicated picture . . . Be general, or specialised. Live fast, or slow. Keep it simple, or don't. Be in the right place at the right time. If all else fails, try becoming a "superspecies", blessed with a physiology that can withstand anything.[13]

To put it another way, Darwinists are ready to ascribe the existence of living fossils to any cause apart from the fact of Creation. If all their explanations fail to hold water, they will then regard a particular organism as a "superspecies," as is clearly stated by New Scientist. The only thing that may not be done, in Darwinist eyes, is to admit that the life form in question was originally "created."

These inconsistent claims—which Darwin hid behind and that present-day Darwinists generally avoid mentioning—have been totally demolished in the face of the extraordinarily large numbers of fossils exhibiting stasis. There are more "living fossils" than evolutionists can dream up scenarios for, and they clearly indicate that evolution never took place.

According to evolutionary theory, an animal resembling a modern-day wolf entered the sea one day, and within 50 million years, its descendants turned into a gigantic marine mammal as the whale.[14] If, despite its evident illogicality, evolution is able to turn a land mammal into a whale in such a relatively brief space of geologic time, how could the salamander remain unchanged for 160 million years? No evolutionist has any scientific answer to that question.

Moreover, this applies not just to the salamander, but also to countless species and examples of living fossils today, and you shall be seeing specimens of these in later chapters of this book. Countless specimens confirm the stasis in the fossil record, as stated by the evolutionist Niles Eldredge, a paleontologist from the American Museum of Natural History:

> Stasis is now abundantly well documented as the preeminent paleontological pattern in the evolutionary history of species.[15]

The specimens discovered prove that millions of years ago, a great many living things had the same anatomical features as they do today. In fact, as much so that 84% of the insect family that existed 100 million years ago is also alive today.[16] The botanist Margaret Helder cites Niles Eldredge's views and describes this magnificent diversity in living fossils thus:

110-million-year-old scorpion and 108- to 92-million-year-old grasshopper fossils show that these creatures have maintained the exact same structures and characteristics for tens of millions of years and that they have never changed. In other words, they have never undergone evolution.

Characterization of an organism as a living fossil basically depends upon the degree of similarity the viewer seeks between living and fossil creatures. If the definition is in terms of general categories of organism, such as sponges in general, or ferns in general, or even specific groups of ferns, then, says Niles Eldredge, ". . . by such a yardstick, virtually everything is a living fossil."[17] Whether one allows one's definition to be this broad or not, it is safe to conclude that living fossils are not rare. [18]

No doubt, the emergence of these life forms in large numbers comes as no surprise to any rational individual. If people can see that God has created all living things, then they can also understand the proofs that manifest themselves in the fossil record. Throughout the history of life, organisms did not evolve, but emerged suddenly and with the most complex and most perfect features.

This goes to show that all living things are created. It is easy for God to create a living thing that exists today with the same astounding characteristics that He also created millions of years ago. For those able to appreciate this, the existence of living fossils is one of the

proofs of God's creation. The Earth provides no evidence of evolution as claimed by Darwin, but confirms the fact of Creation. Niles Eldredge is just one of the evolutionists who admit as much:

> Simple extrapolation does not work. I found that out back in the 1960s as I tried in vain to document examples of the kind of slow, steady directional change we all thought ought to be there, ever since Darwin told us that natural selection should leave precisely such a telltale signal as we collect our fossils up cliff faces. I found instead, that once species appear in the fossil record, they tend not to change much at all. Species remain imperturbably, implacably resistant to chance as a matter of course.[19]

All this goes to show that evolutionist claims along the lines of "evidence in the fossil record," "the evolutionary process," and "gradual or punctuated change in living things" are all mere speculation. Nobody looking at the facts can believe such Darwinian conjecture—speculative claims that are demolished in a more detailed manner in subsequent chapters.

Pierre-Paul Grassé, the world-famous French zoologist and evolutionist, sets out the evolution error in question:

The distinguishing feature of these fossil crabs discovered in Denmark is that they are discovered in round concretions that rise to the surface of the ground at specific times of the year. These fossils, consequently known as "crab balls," generally date back to the Oligocene Period (37 to 23 million years ago).

**54**   *How Fossils Refute Darwinism*

In the same way that the theory of evolution cannot account for the origin of life, it is also helpless in the face of the variety of species.

The "evolution in action" of J. Huxley and other biologists is simply the observation of demographic facts, local fluctuations of genotypes, geographical distributions. Often the species concerned have remained practically unchanged for hundreds of centuries! Fluctuation as a result of circumstances, with prior modification of the genome, does not imply evolution, and we have tangible proof of this in many panchronic species [i.e. living fossils that remain unchanged for millions of years]...[20]

It is essential for governments in countries where living fossil specimens are unearthed to give them prominence and present them to the world as important scientific evidence. Otherwise, a conception that flies in the face of the scientific facts—in other words, the theory of evolution—will continue to enjoy blind support by way of propaganda and deception. The fossil record documenting the history of life on Earth demonstrates that living things never evolved, but appeared suddenly together with all their complex characteristics. In other words, fossils document the fact of Creation.

*Adnan Oktar (Harun Yahya)* **55**

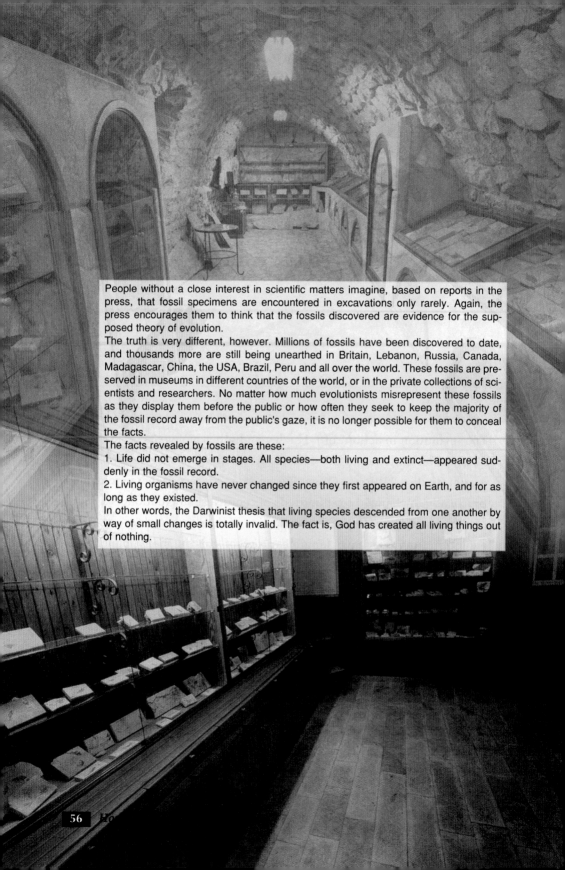

People without a close interest in scientific matters imagine, based on reports in the press, that fossil specimens are encountered in excavations only rarely. Again, the press encourages them to think that the fossils discovered are evidence for the supposed theory of evolution.

The truth is very different, however. Millions of fossils have been discovered to date, and thousands more are still being unearthed in Britain, Lebanon, Russia, Canada, Madagascar, China, the USA, Brazil, Peru and all over the world. These fossils are preserved in museums in different countries of the world, or in the private collections of scientists and researchers. No matter how much evolutionists misrepresent these fossils as they display them before the public or how often they seek to keep the majority of the fossil record away from the public's gaze, it is no longer possible for them to conceal the facts.

The facts revealed by fossils are these:

1. Life did not emerge in stages. All species—both living and extinct—appeared suddenly in the fossil record.

2. Living organisms have never changed since they first appeared on Earth, and for as long as they existed.

In other words, the Darwinist thesis that living species descended from one another by way of small changes is totally invalid. The fact is, God has created all living things out of nothing.

Fossil Specimens Displayed in the Hakel Museum, Lebanon

Selections from the Private Collection of Prof. Robert Cross, Former President of the Proctor Museum of Natural Science

A fossilized sea horse specimen, some 300 million years old

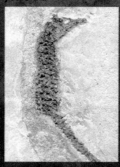

Specimen of a new species of fish, identified for the first time

Three crinoid fossils, some 300 million years old

A frog fossil excavated in China

A fossilized salamander from the Miocene epoch (23 to 5 million years ago) discovered in Germany

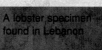

A lobster specimen found in Lebanon

Fossilized remains of a squid

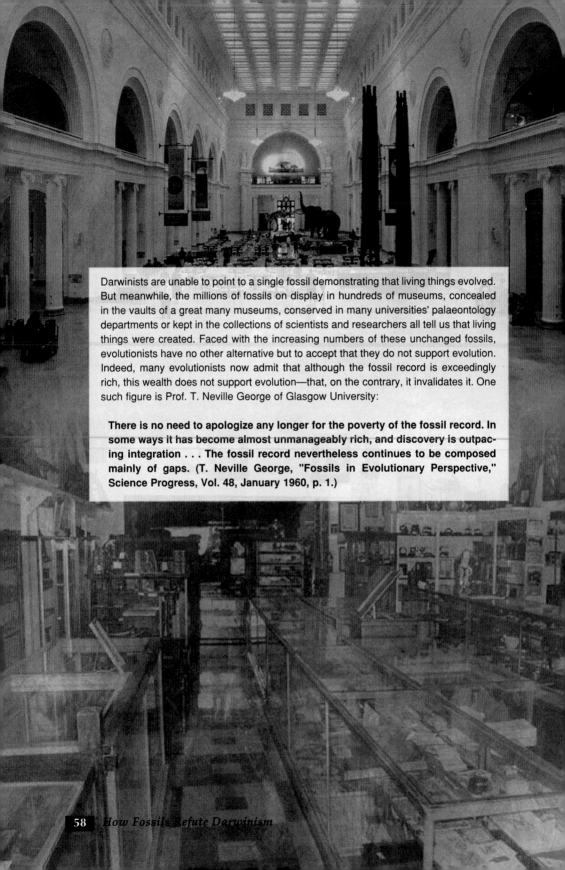

Darwinists are unable to point to a single fossil demonstrating that living things evolved. But meanwhile, the millions of fossils on display in hundreds of museums, concealed in the vaults of a great many museums, conserved in many universities' palaeontology departments or kept in the collections of scientists and researchers all tell us that living things were created. Faced with the increasing numbers of these unchanged fossils, evolutionists have no other alternative but to accept that they do not support evolution. Indeed, many evolutionists now admit that although the fossil record is exceedingly rich, this wealth does not support evolution—that, on the contrary, it invalidates it. One such figure is Prof. T. Neville George of Glasgow University:

**There is no need to apologize any longer for the poverty of the fossil record. In some ways it has become almost unmanageably rich, and discovery is outpacing integration . . . The fossil record nevertheless continues to be composed mainly of gaps. (T. Neville George, "Fossils in Evolutionary Perspective," Science Progress, Vol. 48, January 1960, p. 1.)**

# CENOZOIC
## Georgia Fossils

# CENOZOIC
## Ladds Quarry

# THE *COELACANTH* SILENCED THE SPECULATION CONCERNING FOSSILS

The coelacanth is a large fish some 1.5 meters long. Its entire body is covered with scales, reminiscent of armor plating. It belongs to the Osteoichthyes class of bony fishes, of which the earliest fossils date back to the Devonian Period, 360 to 408 million years ago.

Before 1938, coelacanth fossils were depicted as the solution to a major difficulty for evolutionists. They had not found the slightest trace of any of the millions or even billions of intermediate forms that supposedly must have existed. Evolutionists needed evidence to back up the supposed transition of vertebrates from the sea to dry land. For that reason, they took the fossil coelacanth, whose anatomy they believed was ideally suited to this scenario, and began using it for propaganda purposes. They interpreted the creature's fins as "feet about to walk," and a fossilized fat-filled swimbladder in its body as "a primitive lung." The coelacanth was literally a savior for evolutionists bedeviled by such a lack of evidence. Evolutionists had at last laid hands on "one" of the countless missing links that should have numbered in the millions.

The well known French evolutionist Dr. Jacques Millot, who spent years studying the coelacanth, described how many hid behind it as a lone piece of evidence:

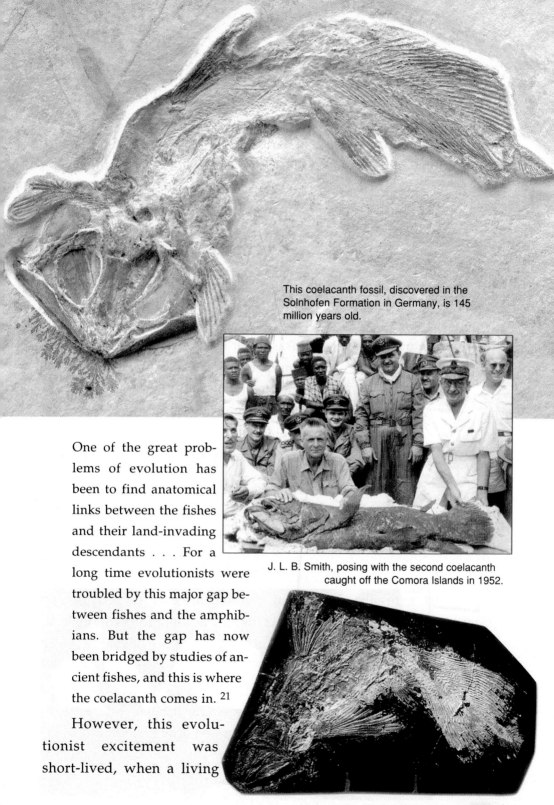

This coelacanth fossil, discovered in the Solnhofen Formation in Germany, is 145 million years old.

J. L. B. Smith, posing with the second coelacanth caught off the Comora Islands in 1952.

One of the great problems of evolution has been to find anatomical links between the fishes and their land-invading descendants . . . For a long time evolutionists were troubled by this major gap between fishes and the amphibians. But the gap has now been bridged by studies of ancient fishes, and this is where the coelacanth comes in. [21]

However, this evolutionist excitement was short-lived, when a living coelacanth specimen was captured by fishermen in 1938. This inflicted a terrible disappointment on evolutionists. James Leonard Brierley Smith, an instructor in the Rhodes University Chemistry Department and also honorary director of various fish museums on the South Coast of England, expressed his astonishment in the face of this captured coelacanth:

> Although I had come prepared, that first sight hit me like a white-hot blast and made me feel shaky and queer, my body tingled. I stood as if striken to stone. Yes, there was not a shadow of doubt, scale by scale, bone by bone, fin by fin, it was true Coelacanth. [22]

The discovery of this imaginary missing link, once believed to have close links to man's alleged ancestors, in the form of a living fossil, was a most significant disaster for Darwinist circles. The coelacanth, the greatest supposed proof of the theory of evolution, had suddenly been demolished. The most important potential candidate in the fictitious transition from the sea to dry land

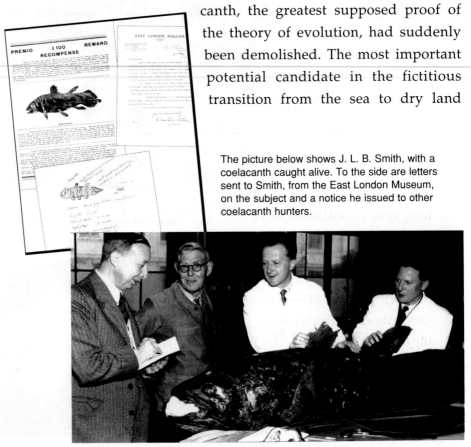

The picture below shows J. L. B. Smith, with a coelacanth caught alive. To the side are letters sent to Smith, from the East London Museum, on the subject and a notice he issued to other coelacanth hunters.

*How Fossils Refute Darwinism*

A 410-MILLION-YEAR OLD
COELACANTH FOSSIL

Many living coelacanths were caught after 1938. It was thus revealed that these fish lived in deep ocean waters and never rose above 180 meters. It emerged that the coelacanth was not, as Darwinists had long claimed, an intermediate form, but a "living fossil" that had survived unchanged for 400 million years.

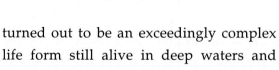

THE COELACANTH IS FISHIS A BOTTOM-DWELLING FISH FOUND IN DEEP WATERS.

turned out to be an exceedingly complex life form still alive in deep waters and bearing no intermediate-form characteristics at all. This living specimen dealt a heavy blow to Darwin's theory of evolution.

When the fish was introduced to the press in the middle of March 1939, articles about it appeared in newspapers and magazines all over the world, from New York to Sri Lanka. Full-size illustrations of the creature were printed in the Illustrated London News. Alongside the picture was an article by Dr. E. I. White of the British Museum. Titled "One of the Most Amazing Events in the Realm of Natural History in the Twentieth Century," the article described the discovery as "sensational" and claimed that the discovery was as as surprising as the finding of a living example of the 2.5-meter-long Mesozoic dinosaur Diplodocus. [23]

J. L. B. Smith conducted countless investigations into the coelacanth in the years that followed, devoting literally his entire life to it.

He led research in various parts of the world in order to find a living coelacanth at the sea bottom and examine its internal organs in detail. (Since the first captured coelacanth was submitted to Smith only long after the event, it had been impossible to preserve its internal organs.)

A second coelacanth was found in later years. However, the fish died soon after being removed from the deep waters in which it lived and brought to the warm, shallow surface waters. Nonetheless it was still possible to examine its internal organs. The reality encountered by the investigating team, led by Dr. Jacques Millot, was very different to that which had been expected. Contrary to expectations, the fish's internal organs had no primitive features at all, and it bore no features of being an intermediate form, nor of a supposedly primitive ancestor. It had no primitive lung, as evolutionists had been claiming. The structure that evolutionist investigators imagined to be a primitive lung was actually a fat-filled swimbladder.[24]

In addition, the fish, which had been portrayed as a precursor of reptiles, about to emerge onto dry land, was a bottom-dwelling animal, living in the depths of the ocean and never rising above 180 meters.[25] Even raising it into shallow water led to its death. Therefore, according to Millot, this creature that should have represented the "missing link" they were searching for lacked all the primitive characteristics of a life form alleged to be undergoing a process of evolution.[26] In other words, the fish was no intermediate form and had lived in the ocean depths with exactly the same complex features for the last 400 million years.

In an article published in Nature magazine, the evolutionist paleontologist Peter Forey said the following:

> The discovery of Latimeria [the scientific name of the coelacanth] raised hopes of gathering direct information on the transition of fish to amphibians, for there was then a long-held belief that coelacanths were close to the ancestry of tetrapods. . . . But studies of the anatomy and physiology of Latimeria have found this theory of relationship to be

wanting and the living coelacanth's reputation as a missing link seems unjustified.[27]

All the coelacanths subsequently encountered and studied in their natural habitats again confirmed this fact, and in an even more explicit manner. The idea that the creature had fins undergoing a process of change to enable it to walk was no more than a deception.

As the German evolutionist and biologist Hans Fricke, from the Max Planck Institute, said, "I confess I'm sorry we never saw a coelacanth walk on its fins."[28]

For Darwinists, the existence and numbers of living fossils was enough of a dilemma all by itself. But when the coelacanth—which they had depicted as an intermediate form and used as propaganda however they chose and portrayed as the "greatest proof of evolution"—turned out to be another living fossil, the problem facing them became a very great difficulty.

This state of affairs did away with all the theories developed by evolutionists regarding living fossils. Darwinists had claimed that in order for a life form to remain unchanged, it had to be "generalized." That is, in order to remain the same, a creature had to be able to live in any environment and feed in every possible way. But with the coelacanth, they were now faced with a highly complex and "specialized" species. The coelacanth lived in deep waters, in a specific environment, and had its own particular way of feeding. This meant that all these claims made by evolutionists were untrue.

How had this fish managed to withstand changes on the Earth during the course of its own history and thus remained unchanged? According to evolutionists, the continents had undergone changes some 250 million years ago—and thus should have had an effect on the coelacanth, which had already been in existence for 150 million years. Yet for some reason, and despite the changes to its environment, the animal exhibited no alterations at all.

Focus magazine described the position as follows:

According to the scientific facts, all the continents were joined together some 250 million years ago. This enormous area of land was surrounded by a single giant ocean. Around 125 million years ago, the Indian Ocean opened up as the result of continents changing places. The volcanic caves in the Indian Ocean, which form a large part of the coelacanth's natural habitat, came about under the influence of this movement of continents. An important truth emerges in the light of all these facts. These animals, which have been in existence for some 400 million years, have remained unchanged despite the many changes in their natural environment![29]

This state of affairs precludes any possibility of further debate

A 240-million-year-old coelacanth fossil found in Madagascar

and confirms that this fish has remained unchanged for millions of years—in other words, that it never evolved. In his book The Story of the Coelacanth, Prof. Keith S. Thomson has this to say on the subject:

> Similarly, for instance, the oldest known Coelacanth (Diplocercides) possessed a rostral organ (the term used by zoologists to refer to the sac filled with a jelly-like substance in the skull, and the six tubes attached to it), a special skull articulation, a hollow spinal chord (notochord) and few teeth. In the same way that this shows that the group has remained almost unchanged since the Devonian Period (for 400 million years), it also reveals that there is a huge gap in the fossil record, since we lack the chain of ancestral fossils showing the emergence of all the common features observed in all coelacanths.[30]

The fossil pictured shows that the coelacanth's scales have been fossilized in considerable detail. To the side can be seen a coelacanth scale. Despite the passage of hundreds of millions of years, no change has taken place in the coelacanth's structure.

# NEW INFORMATION CONCERNING
# THE CŒLACANTH

The latest information concerning the coelacanth's complex structure continues to represent a problem for evolutionists. Professor Michael Bruton, director of the world-renowned South African JLB Smith Institute of Ichthyology, says this about the complex characteristics of the coelacanth that have been discovered:

> Birth is one of the complex features of this creature. Coelacanths bring their young into the world by giving birth to them. The eggs, the size of an orange, hatch inside the fish. The discovery has also been made that the young are fed thanks to an organ in the mother's body resembling a placenta. As well as providing the young with oxygen and food, the placenta is also a complex organ which removes wastes from respiration and digestion from the babies' bodies. Fossil embryos from the Carboniferous period (360-290 million years ago) show that this complex system existed long before mammals appeared.[31]

The discovery that the coelacanth is sensitive to electromagnetic currents around it indicates the presence of a complex sensory organ. Looking at the nerves that connect the fish's rostral organ to its brain, scientists agreed that this organ is responsible for detecting electromagnetic currents. The fact that this perfect organ is present in even the most ancient coelacanth fossils, together with its other complex structures, gives rise to a difficulty that evolutionists are unable to resolve.

The problem was described as follows in Focus magazine:

According to fossils, fish emerged some 470 million years ago. The coelacanth emerged 60 million years after that. It is astonishing that this creature, which would be expected to possess very primitive features, actually has a most complex structure.[32]

For evolutionists expect a gradual evolutionary process. The appearance of the coelacanth with its complex structures, at a time when they expect fictitious primitive life forms to have existed, is of course astonishing. However, for rational people—able to comprehend that God has created all living things and their complex structures in the form and at the time of His choosing—there is nothing at all surprising about it. The flawless specimens created by God are all means whereby we can appreciate His might and power.

A coelacanth caught and frozen in 1966 provided new information about the animal's blood. Apart from the coelacanth, all bony fish (Osteichthyes) meet their water requirements by drinking sea water and expelling the excess salt from their bodies. The coelacanth's system, however, resembles that in cartilaginous fish (Chondrichthyes), which include the shark. The shark converts the ammonia released as the result of the breaking down of proteins into urea, and maintains a level of urea in its bloodstream that would be lethal to human beings. It adjusts the level of these substances in its blood according to the salinity of the water around it. Since the blood assumes an isotonic level with the sea water around it (since the internal and external osmotic pressures are equalized, achieving the same intensity), no water is lost to the outside.

It was revealed that the coelacanth's liver possesses the enzymes necessary to manufacture urea. In other words, it has unique blood properties not found in any other members of its class and that emerged only tens of millions of years later in sharks—members of an entirely different classification.[33] All this goes to show that the coela-

Darwinists experienced a huge shock when a live coelacanth was captured, and were thus once again faced with the fact that their theory was an unscientific one.

*How Fossils Refute Darwinism*

canth, portrayed as the greatest link in the supposed evolution of living things, refutes all evolutionist claims, as do countless specimens still living today.

This example clearly demonstrates the kind of wide-ranging propaganda that evolutionists are capable of, based on a single fossil, and how they are able to disseminate that deception with no concrete evidence. Even after the capture of a living coelacanth, notice that they still did not abandon their claims, but continued looking in the living specimen for "a fin undergoing changes to permit walking." They found no evidence to the effect that the coelacanth, whose complex features clearly show it to have been created, was an intermediate form.

They sought to produce evidence against God, but He eliminated all their false proofs. What there is instead, is proof of an immaculate creation.

# THE STARTING POINT OF PUNCTUATED EQUILIBRIUM

Those who came after Darwin made enormous efforts to detect in the fossil record examples of the slow and gradual evolution that he foresaw. Darwin had ascribed their absence to the "insufficiency of the fossil record." The fossil record—which, in fact, provided a broad range of specimens even in his own day and shows the existence of all complex life forms as early as the Cambrian Explosion—continued to be the subject of research by evolutionists hoping to discover a miracle. Their objective was to prove Darwin correct, to demonstrate that the fossil record in his time truly was insufficient, and to find examples of intermediate forms, evidence that living things did undergo evolution.

Niles Eldredge

Yet the fossil record constantly produced results at variance with Darwin's expectations. Practically the entire globe was scoured, and the new fossils excavated were no

A fictitious illustration

Stephen Jay Gould

longer "insufficient." Darwin had been wrong when he said that he believed that those who came after him would eventually find the intermediate forms that he expected. The fossil record produced not one single intermediate-form specimen. Instead, it revealed the fact that countless living things had undergone no evolution at all, had remained unchanged for many millions of years, together with all their many complex structures. The fossil record refuted Darwin. The lack of intermediate forms and the fact of stasis very definitely constituted no evidence for gradual evolution.

Some evolutionists clearly saw and admitted that Darwin's model of gradual evolution was untenable in the face of the reality of stasis. They then proposed that evolution "operated in a different way." In 1970, the Harvard University paleontologist Stephen Jay Gould and Niles Eldredge of the American Museum of Natural History developed an alternative theory, known as "punctuated evolution," which they published in 1972. Their sole aim was to account for the stasis phenomenon.

"Intermediate forms," which allegedly bore the features of two different species, never existed at any time.

In fact, this theory was an adaptation of the "Hopeful Monster" theory put forward in the 1930s by the European paleontologist Otto Schindewolf. He had suggested that living things evolved as the result of sudden, dramatic mutations rather than the gradual accumulation of small ones. In citing a hypothetical example of his theory, Schindewolf suggested that the first bird in history had emerged from a reptile egg, through a "gross mutation," in other words, an enormous, though random change in its genetic structure.[34] According to that same theory, some terrestrial mammals might suddenly have turned into whales through a sudden and comprehensive alteration.

These claims violate all known laws of genetics, biophysics and biochemistry, and were no more scientific than the fairy tale about a frog turning into a handsome prince. Still, this "Hopeful Monster" theory of Schindewolf's was adopted and defended in the 1940s by the University of California, Berkeley geneticist Richard Goldschmidt. But the theory was so inconsistent that it was soon abandoned.

The impetus that obliged Gould and Eldredge to take up this theory again was, as we have already seen, the lack of any "intermediate form" in the fossil record. Both the "stasis" and "sudden appearance" in the record were so obvious that these two were forced to reconsider the "Hopeful Monster" theory in order to account for this state of affairs. Gould's well-known article "The Return of Hopeful Monsters" was an expression of this forced about-turn. [35]

Naturally, Eldredge and Gould did not repeat Schindewolf's theory word for word. In order to give it a more "scientific" nature, they sought to develop some kind of mechanism for the "sudden evolutionary leap" they proposed. (The interesting term "punctuated equilibrium" which they gave to their theory was one expression of this scientific endeavor.) Gould and Eldredge's theory was adopted and fleshed out by some other paleontologists in the years that followed. However, the punctuated theory of evolution was at least as marred with inconsistencies and invalid logic as Darwin's original gradual theory of evolution.

Proponents of gradual evolution ignored stasis. But stasis is constantly seen in the fossil record, proving that living things remained unchanged over millions of years. The only difference between Gould and Eldredge and other Darwinists is that the former two realized that the stasis in the fossil record was an incontrovertible fact that could no longer be left unanswered. Rather than admit the fact of Creation revealed by the fossil record, they felt themselves obliged to develop a new concept of evolution.

Stephen Jay Gould said this on the subject:

But how can imperfection possibly explain away stasis (the equilibrium of punctuated equilibrium)? Abrupt appearance may record an absences of information, but *stasis is data*. Eldredge and I became so frustrated by the failure of many colleagues to grasp this evident point—-though a quarter century of subsequent debate has finally propelled our claim to general acceptance (while much else about punctuated equilibrium remains controversial)—that we urged the incorporation of this little phrase as a mantra or motto. Say it ten times before breakfast every day for a week, and the argument will surely seep in by osmosis: "stasis is data: stasis is data..." [36]

Gould, Eldredge and other advocates of punctuated evolution fiercely criticized the proponents of gradual evolution for failing to see the reality of stasis. But in fact, what they were doing was no different from the actions of other Darwinists. Since the fossil record had failed to produce the results they expected, they changed the form of so-called evolution and constructed it in a very detailed manner. The main reason for their anger toward, and intense criticism of, the adherents of gradual evolution was that as long as their professional colleagues failed to accept the stasis in the fossil record, they would cause the theory to lose all credibility in the public eye. For that reason, they attempted to give the impression that they had now "discovered the truth" in the face of the clear facts revealed by the fossil record.

The fact is, however, that the punctuated evolution model is at least as groundless, devoid of evidence, and ultimately discredited as the gradual evolution theory.

Gould's admissions regarding "the mistaken perspective in the past" are criticisms aimed at the supporters of gradual evolution:

> We have long known about stasis and abrupt appearance, but have chosen to fob it off upon an imperfect fossil record.[37]

Comme le décrit Niles Eldredge, les avocats de l'évolution graduelle ignoraient un point très important:

> Paleontologists ever since Darwin have been searching (largely in vain) for the sequences of insensibly graded series of fossils that would stand as examples of the sort of wholesale transformation of species that Darwin envisioned as the natural product of the evolutionary process. Few saw any reason to demur—though it is a startling fact that . . . most species remain recognizably themselves, virtually unchanged throughout their occurrence in geological sediments of various ages.[38]

Niles Eldredge and the archaeologist Ian Tattershall of the American Museum of Natural History underlined how Darwin's idea of evolution had been disproved by the stasis in the fossil record:

> Darwin's prediction of rampant, albeit gradual, change affecting all lin-

This 120-million-year-old fossil tortoise is proof that tortoises are not descended from other living things, never underwent any intermediate stages, and have maintained exactly the same structure for millions of years.

eages through time is refuted. The record is there, and the record speaks for tremendous anatomical conservation. Change in the manner Darwin expected is just not found in the fossil record.[39]

Elsewhere, Stephen Jay Gould described how stasis, evidence of non-evolution, was ignored by the adherents of evolution:

Stasis, or nonchange, of most fossil species during their lengthy geological lifespans was tacitly acknowledged by all paleontologists, but almost never studied explicitly because prevailing theory treated stasis as uninteresting nonevidence for nonevolution. . . . The overwhelming prevalence of stasis became an embarrassing feature of the fossil record, best left ignored as a manifestation of nothing (that is, nonevolution).[40]

All of Gould and Eldredge's efforts were to adapt the theoretical concept of evolution to the actual fossil record. For that reason they suggested that stasis itself was the most important proof of their evolutionary claims. In some way, they viewed the unchanging nature of the fossil record as evidence for change! Since they could not reconcile the fossil record with the theory of evolution, they adapted the theory to the record. This was the mindset that launched the punctuated model of evolution.

In an article in New Scientist, Tom S. Kemp, curator of the Oxford University museum's zoological collections, described how findings had been turned into evidence for the theory of evolution, just as in the case of punctuated evolution:

> In other words, when the assumed evolutionary processes did not match the pattern of fossils that they were supposed to have generated, the pattern was judged to be 'wrong.' A circular argument arises: interpret the fossil record in terms of a particular theory of evolution, inspect the interpretation, and note that it confirms the theory. Well, it would, wouldn't it?[41]

According to the proponents of the punctuated model of evolution, stasis in the fossil record represented the "equilibrium" in the theory defined as punctuated equilibrium. The theory maintains that under environmental pressures, a species can have evolved in as short a space of time as only a few thousand years. It then entered a period of stasis and remained unchanged for millions of years.

Therefore, proponents believed that this claim could account for the stasis in a large proportion of living things. In this way, they thought they had covered up the challenge that the fossil record poses to evolution. But this was a grave deception.

## The Punctuation Mechanism

In its present state, the punctuated theory of evolution explains living populations that exhibit no change over very long periods of time as having remained in a kind of "equilibrium." According to this claim, evolutionary changes take place in very narrow populations and at very short intervals that interrupt—or in other words, "punctuate" the equilibrium. Since the population is such a narrow one, natural selection quickly favors large mutations, and the emergence of a new species is thus made possible.

According to this theory, a reptile species, for example, can remain unchanged for millions of years. However, one small group of reptiles that split away from this species in some way is subjected to a series of intense mutations, for some reason that is not explained. These mutations endow those individuals with some advantage (and there is no instance of a beneficial mutation). They are quickly selected within this narrow group. The group of reptiles evolves quickly, and may even turn into mammals. Since this entire process is so very rapid and takes place with a relatively small num-

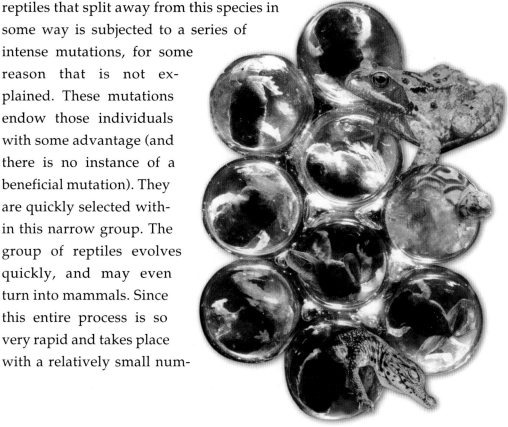

ber of creatures within a narrow time frame, few if any fossil traces are left behind.

As close inspection reveals, this theory was proposed as an answer to the question of "How can an evolutionary process happen so fast as to leave no fossil traces behind?" In reply, the theory makes two fundamental assumptions:

1. The assumption that macro-mutations—in other words, wide-ranging mutations that cause major changes in living things' genetic information—bestow an advantage and also produce new genetic information.

2. The assumption that small animal populations have a genetic advantage.

However, both are at odds with the scientific facts.

## The Macro-Mutations Error

As you have just seen, the punctuated model of evolution hypothesizes that the mutations leading to speciation take place on a very large scale or that some individual species are exposed to a succession of serial mutations. However, that assumption contradicts all the observational data from genetic science.

R. A. Fisher, one of the century's best-known geneticists, established a rule, based on experiment and observation, that invalidates this hypothesis. In his book The Genetical Theory of Natural Selection, Fisher reports that any mutation's ability to survive in a population is inversely proportional to its effect on the phenotype.[42] To put it another way, the greater a mutation is, the lower will be its chances of remaining permanent in a community.

The reason for this is not hard to see. Mutations represent random changes in a living thing's genetic data. They never have the effect of improving that genetic information. On the contrary, mutated individuals always suffer serious diseases and disabilities.

Therefore, the more any individual is affected by mutation, the lower its chances of survival.

The Harvard University evolutionary biologist Ernst Mayr, one of Darwinism's most passionate advocates, makes the following comment:

> The occurrence of genetic monstrosities by mutation . . . is well substantiated, but they are such evident freaks that these monsters can be designated only as "hopeless." They are so utterly unbalanced that they would not have the slightest chance of escaping elimination through stabilizing selection . . . the more drastically a mutation affects the phenotype, the more likely it is to reduce fitness. To believe that such a drastic mutation would produce a viable new type, capable of occupying a new adaptive zone, is equivalent to believing in miracles . . . The finding of a suitable mate for the "hopeless monster" and the establishment of reproductive isolation from the normal members of the parental population seem to me insurmountable difficulties.[43]

Obviously, mutations do not give rise to evolutionary development—which poses an insurmountable obstacle for the punctuated theory of evolution. Since mutation is destructive, the living undergoing macro-mutations that the proponents of evolution propose will suffer "macro"-destructive effects. Some evolutionists put their trust in mutations occurring in the regulatory genes in DNA. But the destructive effect that applies in regard to other mutations also

applies here. The problem is that mutation is a random change, and any random change in any structure as complex as genetic information will have damaging consequences.

In their book The Natural Limits to Genetic Change, geneticist Lane Lester and population geneticist Raymond Bohlin describe the mutation dilemma in question:

> The overall factor that has come up again and again is that mutation remains the ultimate source of all genetic variation in any evolutionary model. Being unsatisfied with the prospects of accumulating small point mutations, many are turning to macromutations to explain the origin of evolutionary novelties. Goldschmidt's hopeful monsters have indeed returned. However, though macromutations of many varieties produce drastic changes, the vast majority will be incapable of survival, let alone show the marks of increasing complexity. If structural gene mutations are inadequate because of their inability to produce significant enough changes, then regulatory and developmental mutations appear even less useful because of the greater likelihood of nonadaptive or even destructive consequences . . . But one thing seems certain: at present, the thesis that muta-

tions, whether great or small, are capable of producing limitless biological change is more an article of faith than fact.[44]

Observation and experiment show that mutations may alter, but do not improve on, genetic information and that they do damage living things. It is obviously inconsistent for the proponents of punctuated evolution to expect any "success" from them.

## The Narrow Populations Error

The second concept that proponents of punctuated evolution stress is that of "narrow populations." They state that a new species forms only in communities containing very few numbers of a plant or animal species. According to this claim, large populations of animals exhibit no evolutionary development and can maintain their stasis. However, if some small groups leave these populations, they become

isolated (generally assumed because of geographical causes) and can reproduce only amongst themselves. It is claimed that macro-mutations affect these small groups because they reproduce only among themselves, and so rapid "speciation" thus takes place.

Why do the proponents of punctuated evolution insist on the concept of narrow populations? The answer is obvious: Their objective is to "explain" the lack of intermediate forms in the fossil record. That is why their accounts insist that "Evolutionary changes took place in narrow populations and very rapidly, for which reason insufficient traces have been left in the fossil record."

In fact, however, recent scientific experiments and observations have revealed that in genetic terms, narrow populations are a disadvantage for evolution. Far from developing in such a way as to give rise to robust new species, narrow populations actually produce severe genetic defects. The reason is that in small populations, individuals continually interbreed, reproducing within a narrow genetic pool. For that reason, normally "heterozygotic" individuals become increasingly "homozygotic." Their normally recessive defective genes become dominant, and genetic defects and diseases increasingly emerge within the population. [45]

In order to investigate this topic, chickens were observed for 35 years. These observations established that chickens kept in a narrow population became increasingly weaker in genetic terms. Egg production fell from 100% to 80%; reproduction rates from 93% to 74%. But through conscious human intervention—with chickens being brought in from other populations—this genetic contraction was reversed, and the basic chicken population began moving back in the direction of normality. [46]

This and similar findings clearly show that there is no scientific validity to the claim that narrow populations are the source of evolutionary development, behind which adherents of punctuated evolution find shelter. James W. Valentine and Douglas H. Erwin have stated the impossibility of new species forming by way of punctuated evolutionary mechanisms:

> The required rapidity of the change implies either a few large steps or many and exceedingly rapid smaller ones. Large steps are tantamount to saltations and raise the problems of fitness barriers; small steps must be numerous and entail the problems discussed under microevolution. The periods of stasis raise the possibility that the lineage would enter the fossil record, and we reiterate that we can identify none of the postulated intermediate forms. Finally, the large numbers of species that must be generated so as to form a pool from which the successful lineage is selected are nowhere to be found. We conclude that the probability that species selection is a general solution to the origin of higher taxa is not great, and that neither of the contending theories of evolutionary change at the species level, phyletic gradualism or punctuated equilibrium, seem applicable to the origin of new body plans.[47]

A 150-million-year-old fossil brittlestar showing that these echinoderms have not changed at all for millions of years.

# Punctuated Equilibrium is a Major Disappointment for Evolutionists

Today, the fictitious mechanism of punctuated equilibrium has been totally discredited in scientific terms. It has been proved that living things cannot evolve through the methods in question. As Jeffrey Levinton from the State University of New York has stated, there can be no way to test the theory of species formation in question if it cannot be seen clearly in the fossil record. On that basis, Levinton concluded that "the totality of the evidence makes it a theory not worth following up."[48]

This is of course true. The claim constituting the foundation of the theory has been refuted scientifically. But the important fact is that the

There is no difference between this 50-million-year-old fossil trout-perches and specimens living today.

There is no difference between lobsters living today and this 208- to 146-million-year-old fossil.

fossil record has provided no evidence for punctuated equilibrium; on the contrary, it has demolished it. Millions of fossils in the record have been in a state of "equilibrium" that the evolutionists claim to have lasted for millions of years, as punctuated equilibrium suggests. Yet for some reason, there is absolutely no trace of the intervening evolution that—again according to the theory—should have lasted for thousands of years, at least. The fossil record provides not one single example of the countless living things expected to have undergone evolution. Nor is there a single piece of evidence to show how punctuated equilibrium might work. As the result of their desperate situation, evolutionists try to take one of the greatest proofs of the fact of Creation and use it as a basis for evolution. This clearly demonstrates the terrible position they are in!

How did such an inconsistent theory ever become so popular? In fact, almost all the proponents of punctuated equilibrium are paleontologists, who clearly see how the fossil record refutes Darwinian theory.

This is why they are literally in a state of panic and trying to keep their theory viable at any cost.

On the other hand, geneticists, zoologists and anatomists

perceive that no mechanism in nature could give rise to "punctuations," for which reason they insist on supporting the gradual Darwinist theory of evolution. The Oxford University zoologist Richard Dawkins strongly criticizes adherents of the punctuated model of evolution and accuses them of destroying the credibility of the theory as a whole.

This inconclusive dialogue between the two sides is actually evidence of the scientific crisis into which the theory of evolution has fallen. What we have is a myth that cannot be reconciled with any experimental, observational or paleontological findings. All evolutionist theoreticians look for grounds to support this myth, depending on their own field of specialization, but find themselves in conflict with findings from other branches of science. Attempts are sometimes made to gloss over this confusion by means of superficial comments such as "Science advances through such academic debates." Yet the problem is that these debates are not mental gymnastics performed for the sake of coming up with any true scientific theory, but are dogmatic conjecture intended to support a false theory. The fact that evolutionary theoreticians inadvertently reveal is that the fossil record cannot be reconciled with the concept of evolution in any way. And stasis, one of the most important elements in the fossil record, is clearly visible. Gould expresses this in these terms:

One important characteristic of the insects that appear suddenly in the fossil record, together with all their flawless structures, is their extraordinary flight techniques. These marvelous flying insects have had the same wing architecture since they were first created as they have today, 125 million years later. They have never undergone any evolution. This beetle that lived 125 million years ago was petrified in stone together with all its fine detail.

. . . stasis, inevitably read as absence of evolution, had always been treated as a non-subject. How odd though to define the most common of all palaeontological phenomena as beyond interest or notice![49]

By now, all Darwinists have been forced to admit the fact of stasis in the fossil record, which they are still reluctant to see, deliberately pushing into the background and even refusing to accept as data. The lack of any documentation of fossils undergoing evolution—in other words, the absence of any intermediate forms—has done away with all speculation regarding stasis and clearly reveals this as one of the most significant proofs of the fact of Creation. Punctuated equilibrium has been totally discredited, both by the very mechanisms it proposes and by the fossil record, which it seeks to put forward as evidence.

# CAMBRIAN FOSSILS AND THE CREATION OF SPECIES

The oldest of the Earth's strata in which the fossils of complex life forms appear were laid down in the Cambrian Period, estimated at between 543 and 490 million years ago. In strata older than the Cambrian, no fossils of living things are found, apart from single-celled organisms. In the Cambrian Period, however, a variety of distinctly different life forms suddenly appeared. More than 30 life forms, such as sea urchins, starfish, trilobites, snails and fish appeared in a single moment.

Furthermore, contrary to the assumptions of the theory of evolution, all of the life forms that appeared so suddenly possess highly complex physical structures, not simple "rudimentary" ones.

According to the erroneous theory of evolution, more sophisticated life forms must have evolved from other, more primitive ones. Yet there are no complex life forms at all prior to those of the Cambrian Period. These Cambrian life forms appeared all at once, with not a single earlier forerunner. The British zoologist Richard Dawkins, the best-known living proponent of the theory of evolution, admits that:

> It is as though they [Cambrian creatures] were just planted there, without any evolutionary history.[50]

This fact definitively invalidates the theory of evolution. Because in *The Origin of Species*, Darwin wrote:

> If numerous species, belonging to the same genera or families, have really started into life all at once, the fact would be fatal to the theory of descent with slow modification through natural selection.[51]

This lethal blow that Darwin so feared came from the Cambrian Period, at the very beginning of the fossil record.

New life forms also appeared suddenly and with complete, flawless structures in the ages after the Cambrian. Basic groups such as fish, amphibians, reptiles, birds and mammals each appeared on Earth in a single moment and in flawless forms. Not a single intermediate form of the kind hoped for by evolutionists exists among them.

Trilobite eye

A 380-MILLION-YEAR OLD TRILOBITE FOSSIL

Trilobites are some of the most abundant life forms to have emerged in the Cambrian period. They lived in various parts of the world.

One of the most astonishing characteristics of trilobites is their multi-lens eye, made up of numerous units, each unit being a separate lens. Each lens perceives a different image, and these are then combined as a whole "picture." Research has shown that there were more than 3,000 lenses in the trilobite eye, which meant the creature received more than 3000 images. This, in turn, clearly reveals how perfect were the eye and brain structure of this creature that lived nearly 530 million years ago. Such a flawless structure could not possibly have emerged by way of evolution.

This fact revealed by the fossil record proves that living things have not evolved from the simple to the more complex, neither functionally nor in terms of appearance, but were created by God. The evolutionist Mark Czarnecki admits as much:

A major problem in proving the theory has been the fossil record; the imprints of vanished species preserved in the Earth's geological formations. This record has never revealed traces of Darwin's hypothetical intermediate variants—instead species appear ... abruptly, and this anomaly has fueled the creationist argument that each species was created by God.[52]

# "MISSING LINK DISCOVERED" HEADLINES ARE AN UNSCIENTIFIC DECEPTION

If you've ever read a newspaper headline announcing the discovery of a "missing link," then you can be certain that the report has no scientific value. Serious scientists long ago abandoned the idea of "missing links" and accepted that it is unscientific to make evolutionary conjectures based on fossils.

Henry Gee, a paleontologist and editor of the scientific journal Nature, writes this on the subject in his 1999 book In Search of Deep Time:

> Given the ubiquitous chatter of journalists and headline writers about the search for ancestors, and the discovery of missing links, it may come as a surprise to learn that most professional palaeontologists do not think of the history of life in terms of scenarios or narratives, and that they rejected the storytelling mode of evolutionary history as unscientific more than thirty years ago.[53]

These persistent reports about missing links aim to give the impression that simply making a discovery will confirm the hypothesis that one species develops into another. Yet excavations over the last century and more have left totally unfounded the expectations that intermediate forms between species would be discovered. The eminent palaeontologist A. S. Romer admitted this as far back as 1963:

"Links" are missing just where we most fervently desire them [to point to a transition between species] and it is all too probable that many "links" will continue to be missing.[54]

Paleontologists have kept their missing links on the "missing list." Yet their own admissions run contrary to the impression that certain media outlets seek to give. For example, Niles Eldredge, and Ian Tattersall lack the media's positive air of expectation:

> One of the most pervasive myths in all of paleontology...is the myth that the evolutionary histories of living beings are essentially a matter of discovery. ... But if this were really so, one could confidently expect that as more hominid fossils were found the story of human evolution would become clearer. Whereas if anything, the opposite has occurred.[55]

Pro-Darwinist reports appearing so frequently in the evolutionist media consist of conjecture and propaganda. These reports are written to conceal the fact that Darwinism has been defeated.

To sum up, the missing link is not a creature waiting to be discovered, but an idea that palaeontologists have long since abandoned, and which cannot be the subject of any truly scientific inquiry. Therefore, why is it the subject of so much insistent propaganda?

The answer to this question lies in the world-view espoused by the theory of evolution. Materialists and atheists have attempted to keep Darwin's theory alive ever since he first put it forward in the mid-19th century. Because although the theory is based on a completely imaginary scenario, materialists seized on it as a supposedly scientific hypothesis.

The evolutionist thinker Mary Midgley expresses this:

> It [the theory of evolution] is, and cannot help being, also a powerful folk-tale about human origins. ... Suggestions about how we were made and where we come from are bound to engage our imagination, to shape our views of what we now are, and so to affect our lives.[56]

At the end of his biology text book *Life on Earth*, the Darwinist biologist Edward O. Wilson makes this admission on the subject of evolutionist claims:

> Every generation needs its own creation myths, and these are ours.[57]

"Missing link" propaganda is therefore a deception intended to keep the evolutionary myth about the origins alive and influential. Evolutionary propaganda is the most important vehicle materialists have for spreading their views. The concept of the "missing link" is key in terms of Darwin's fictitious idea of all species being traceable to common ancestors. Therefore, the more that evolutionists can keep their concept in the spotlight, the more support they hope to muster for their materialist views. That is behind all their efforts to distract the public from the collapse of Darwinism by means of "missing link" headlines.

Despite the evolutionist media's best endeavors, the fossils they describe are not missing links, and neither can anything about them confirm Darwin's theory. These "news" reports consist solely of unscientific speculation regarding newly discovered fossils of extinct species. Yet this unscientific propaganda will not alter the fact that evolutionist scientists themselves admit that there is no scientific basis to the concept of the missing link, nor is there any trace of intermediate forms in the fossil record. The reality that the fossil record reveals is that evolution never occurred.

Illustration factice

People are conditioned to believe in these imaginary entities, as if they were real.

# DARWIN'S ILLOGICAL AND UNSCIENTIFIC FORMULA

When the subject of evolution comes up, many people imagine that this is a scientific problem—and that for anyone less knowledgeable than scientists, Darwinism is impossible to understand. They assume it's pointless to argue the issue, one way or the other. Indeed, Darwinists employ Latin words and scientific terms generally unfamiliar to the public in order to encourage this mistaken idea. They engage in complicated descriptions and frequently resort to demagoguery and hollow slogans in order to give the impression they are discussing a highly scientific matter.

Darwinism's can be espressed in these terms:
Planty of muddy water + A long time + An abundance of coincidences = Civilization

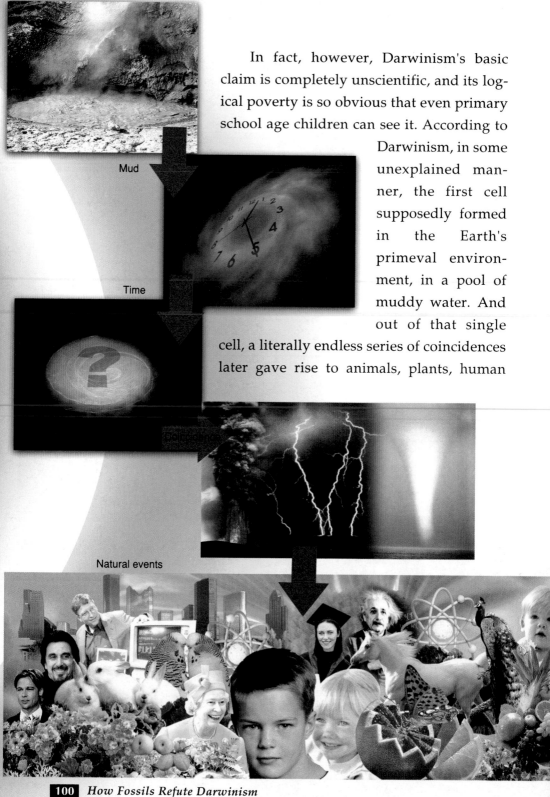

In fact, however, Darwinism's basic claim is completely unscientific, and its logical poverty is so obvious that even primary school age children can see it. According to Darwinism, in some unexplained manner, the first cell supposedly formed in the Earth's primeval environment, in a pool of muddy water. And out of that single cell, a literally endless series of coincidences later gave rise to animals, plants, human

Mud

Time

Natural events

beings and civilizations. In other words, all of mankind, as well as the entire plant and animal kingdoms, are supposedly the work of an ideal quantity of mud, a long period of time and plentiful coincidences.

According to Darwinists, who are suffering from an obvious logical deficiency, these materials, each one of which is unconscious, gave rise to human beings possessed of reason and conscience, who think, love, feel compassion, possess sound judgment, produce paintings and statues, compose symphonies, write novels, build skyscrapers, construct nuclear reactors, discover the causes of diseases and manufacture drugs to cure them, or engage in politics. They claim that when sufficient time had passed, lions, tigers, rabbits, deer, elephants, cats, dogs, moths, flies, crocodiles and birds all evolved by chance from muddy water. A whole range of fruits and vegetables, with their own unique tastes and smells—oranges, strawberries, bananas, apples, grapes, tomatoes, peppers—flowers with their matchless appearances and other plants all emerged from that same mud.

In short, ever since Darwin's time, countless articles, papers, films, newspaper reports, magazine articles and television programs have repeated the evolutionist scenario in which all of life emerged by chance from mud. In other words, if you ask a Darwinist "How did our civilization arise?" or, "How did such a wide range of life forms come into being?" or, "How did mankind come into existence?" the essential answer you will receive is this: Coincidences gave rise to all these things from mud, over the course of time.

One would doubtless need to be devoid of reason or lack any facility for understanding in order to believe such a tale. Yet surprisingly, that very irrational and illogical theory has had its adherents for many years and is still being propagated constantly under a scientific guise.

# The Lies of Darwinism Have Been Unmasked

The theory of evolution, first proposed under the primitive conditions of the 19th century, has been disproved by advances in science and technology. It has been recognized that Darwin's claims are totally unrealistic: Natural selection and mutations, cited as the mechanisms that drive the process of evolution, have no effects of the kind envisaged by Darwinists. In short, it is impossible for them to give rise to new species.

The final death blow to Darwinism was dealt by the fossil record. Darwin claimed that all the millions of different life forms had come into being through descent from a supposed single common ancestor. In order for his claim to be verified, there should be traces in the fossil record—an irrefutable document of natural history—of this supposed

Crocodiles are one example of living fossils. They appeared with all their physical structures fully formed and have survived down to the present day without undergoing any change at all over a period of around 100 million years (there are crocodile fossils dating back 140 million years). The fact that there is no difference betwen the 100-million-year-old fossil crocodile in the picture and those alive today once again emphasizes this fact.

primitive ancestor and of the various life forms that developed from it. For example, if all mammals were descended from reptiles, as evolutionists maintain, then there would have to be fossil remains of a series of half-mammalian, half-reptilian life forms. To date, millions of fossils, belonging to a great many species, have been unearthed during excavations. Yet not a single one showing a transition between species has ever been found. Every fossil ever found shows that each living thing emerged suddenly, with all its characteristics complete. In other words, every species of plant and animal was created.

Confronted by this fact, evolutionists have resorted to various falsehoods. They have produced hoaxes—counterfeit, artificial fossils that have come to be regarded as disgraces to paleontology. They have tried to deceive the lay public by tampering with genuine fossils of extinct life forms and inventing a series of imaginary scenarios.

One of the best known of them is the so-called "evolution of the horse." Fossils belonging to entirely different species that once lived in India, South America, North America and Europe were arranged in order of size—from small to large—in the light of evolutionist imaginations. So far, different researchers have come up with more than 20 different equine evolution scenarios.

There is no agreement among them regarding all these completely different family trees. The one point they commonly agree upon is their belief that a dog-like creature known as Eohippus (or Hyracotherium) that lived in the Eocene epoch (54 to 37 million years ago) was the very first ancestor of today's horses. However, Eohippus—portrayed as the ancestor of the horse and that became extinct millions of years ago—is almost identical to the present-day animal known as the hyrax, which looks nothing like a horse and is totally unrelated to that species.[58]

Moreover, it has been established that breeds of horse living today have also been discovered in the same rock strata as Eohippus. [59] This means that the horse and its supposed ancestor were both living at the same time, which proves that the horse never underwent any such process as evolution.

The invalidity of the "equine series" proposed by evolutionists also applies to birds, fish, reptiles and mammals, in short, to all living things, to their supposedly common ancestors and supposed family trees. It has been determined that every fossil species suggested as being the ancestor of some other living thing either belongs to an independent extinct life form or is the result of evolutionists tampering with fossils of the species in question.

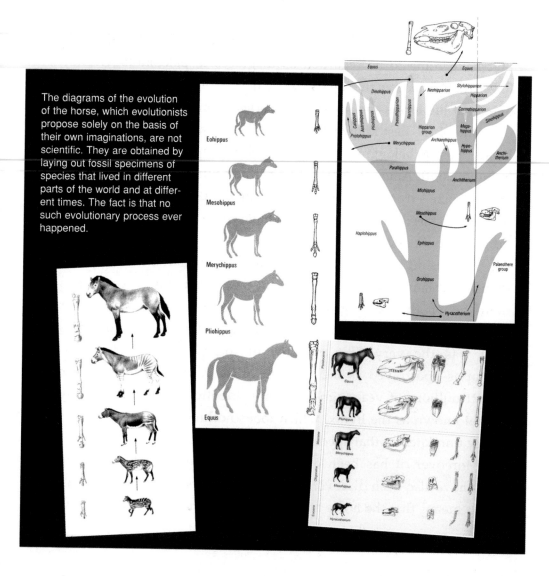

The diagrams of the evolution of the horse, which evolutionists propose solely on the basis of their own imaginations, are not scientific. They are obtained by laying out fossil specimens of species that lived in different parts of the world and at different times. The fact is that no such evolutionary process ever happened.

Using the skulls of extinct apes and various races of humans that once lived in the past, evolutionists seek to establish an imaginary family tree. However, the scientific evidence denies them the opportunity.

## Satan's Game Has Been Exposed

Darwinism has been exposed as the most wide-ranging and astonishing deception in the world's history. That millions have been taken in by this deception, as if hypnotized, and have been influenced by all of Darwinism's illogical claims, is truly miraculous. The support lent to the theory of evolution and the acceptance it has enjoyed up to now are the result of tricks played on mankind by satan, who urges vast numbers of people towards Darwinism.

Until recently, no one had the courage to unmask this ruse of satan's and to publicize the true facts. But in the present century, the response to this deception has finally been laid out in full detail, and the public has been made fully aware of the state of affairs. By the will of God, the collapse of Darwinism has advanced beyond any point of recovery. Indeed, that is the fundamental reason for the panic in the Darwinian global empire.

# CONCLUSION

Why, in his *Origin of Species,* did Darwin refer to living fossils as causing such a great difficulty? Why, faced with these fossils, did evolutionist scientists feel the need to abandon their claims regarding gradual evolution and manufacture a new theory? Why did the capture of a living coelacanth come as such a disappointment, silencing those evolutionists who had pinned all their hopes on it? What is it about living fossils that has inflicted such a collapse on Darwinists?

It is that living fossils declare the fact of Creation.

The disappointment that Darwinists feel is due to their ideological devotion to their theories. In fact, they have seen their theory demolished, but ignore this, even though they are perfectly well aware of it. That they even resort to deceptive methods to cover it up is one of the greatest proofs of this. Instead of admitting the fact of Creation in the face of living fossils, they resort to irrational, illogical theories devoid of any scientific evidence. They seek to conceal living fossil specimens and eliminate millions of examples, while giving pride of place to hand-made hoaxes—a clear indication of their fears. The way that museums display countless fabricated fossil "reconstructions" and depict highly complex life forms like the coelacanth as examples of intermediate forms, while hiding away in the museum vaults fossils of species that still exist today is most thought-provoking.

How scientific is it to adapt evidence to a theory, when the theory cannot be proven? By what right do evolutionists suggest that their claims are proven and scientific, even though they have no evidence whatsoever? Why does the scientific evidence they come up with embarrass them instead of supporting them? What compels evolutionists to stand by their theory, despite the increasing weight of evidence against it?

The reason is that Darwinism is a false religion and system of beliefs. Because it is a dogma that can never be denied. Because it is the basis of materialist philosophy that maintains that matter has existed for all time, and that nothing exists apart from matter. That is why, although new scientific evidence further disproves the theory with every passing day, such efforts are maintained to keep it alive. Yet these have now come to an end. The deceptive methods of Darwinism and Darwinists have failed. The evidence that demolishes evolution is mounting day by day. New proofs of Creation that dash evolutionists' hopes and force them to produce new misleading explanations are constantly emerging.

That is why living fossils leave Darwinists speechless, and are quietly hidden away in museum vaults. With these methods, Darwinists try to conceal God's sublime artistry. The fact is, however, that God is He Who creates all things, Who knows all that they do, and Who keeps them under His rule at all times. God sees Darwinists as they make their plans against Him. God watches them as they seek to conceal His sublime creative artistry. He writes down all they do as they deny His existence. And, whether they believe it or not, willingly or unwillingly, they will be brought into His presence in the Hereafter.

This is the great truth of which Darwinists are unaware: God will surely baffle and disappoint those who strive against Him. It is the law of God that will truly be victorious.

The existence of living fossils is a sublime proof created by God in order to eliminate all Darwinist strategies and reveal all their frauds. As they strive against the true faith, Darwinists forget that God also creates the evidence for it. They are in a state of defeat from the very outset. The teaching of the theory of evolution in schools, speculation regarding evolutionist claims by various media organizations, and the support gathered from scientists are all temporary phenomena. As revealed in the verse: **"Rather We hurl the truth against falsehood and it cuts right through it and it vanishes clean away! Woe without end for you for what you portray!"** (Surat al-'Anbiya, 18), God will eradicate all false beliefs.

Darwinists today are in a state of panic about this. Since that is so obvious, those who imagine Darwinism to be true must quickly try to see all the evidence pointing to the fact of Creation and to avoid being taken in by such a false religion as the theory of evolution. They must realize that God, Who created the world in such a flawless form, also has the power to create the eternal life of the Hereafter, because human beings can be saved only when they see and comprehend this truth. The theory of evolution, which induces people to deny God, their one Savior, and which strives to survive through constant lies and strategies, is a terrible waste of time and a terrible disappointment. Instead of realizing this in a state of great regret in the Hereafter, seeing it in this world, where all the proofs are so evident, will lead to salvation in both this world and in the Next.

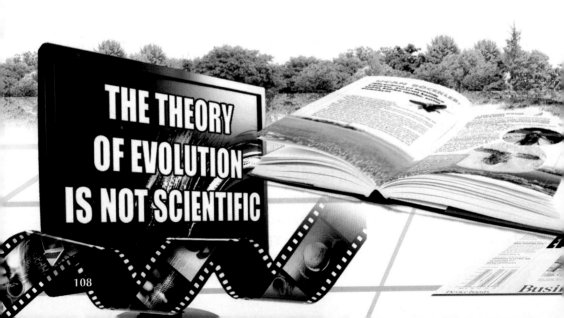

What, then, of Him Who is standing over every self seeing everything it does? Yet still they associate others with God! Say: "Name them! Or would you inform Him of something in the earth He does not know, or are they words which are simply guesswork on your part?" However, the plotting of those who disbelieve seems good to them and they bar the way. Anyone misguided by God has no guide. They will receive punishment in the life of this world and the punishment of the Hereafter is harsher still. They have no defender against God. What is the Garden promised to those who guard against evil like? It has rivers flowing under it and its foodstuffs and cool shade never fail. That is the final fate of those who guard against evil. But the final fate of the unbelievers is the Fire. (Surat ar-Ra'd, 33-35)

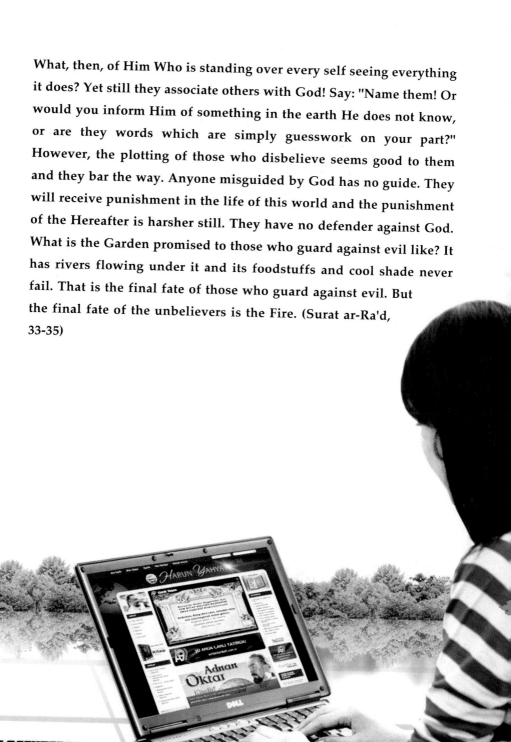

# Fossil Specimens of
# Sea Creatures

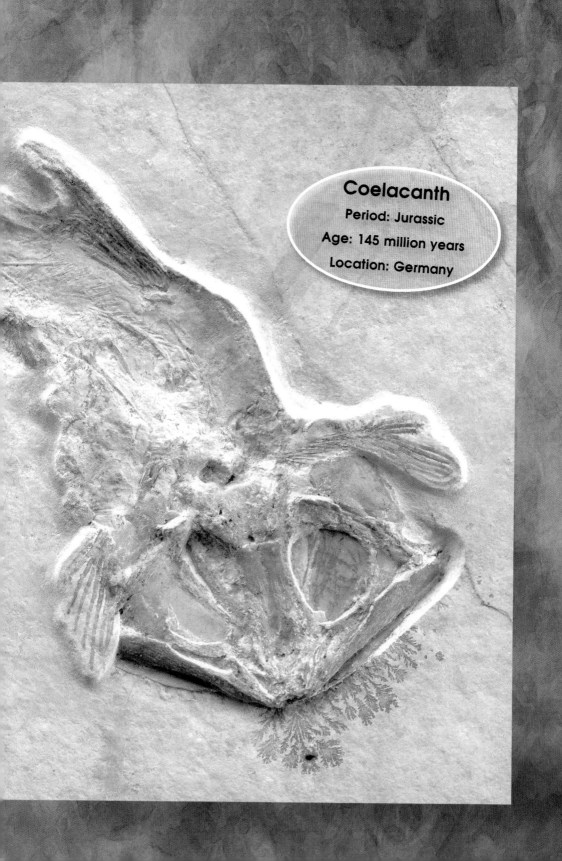

**Coelacanth**

Period: Jurassic

Age: 145 million years

Location: Germany

## Sardine

**Period: Eocene**

**Age: 54-37 million years**

**Region: USA**

Sardines live in shoals. Several sardines have been petrified at the same time in this 54 to 37-million-year fossil. The fossil is evidence that sardines were created in a single moment, together with all their characteristics, and that they have not altered over tens of millions of years.

The head structure, the small fins on top of and underneath its body and the forked tail can all be seen very clearly in the fossil. Like all life forms in the universe, sardines are the work of our Omniscient and Almighty Lord

Starfish generally live on the sea floor, and some species live at depths of 7,000 meters. Evolutionists are in a hopeless position when faced with these echinoderms, which have survived unchanged for around half a billion years. These creatures have remained exactly the same, not for 10 million or 100 million years, nor even for 200 million, but for roughly 500 million years.

If evolutionists' claims were true, then starfish should long since have turned into different life forms over the course of 500 million years, and the remains of many odd-looking creatures, halfstarfish and partly some other invertebrate, should be visible in the fossil record. Yet the fossil record contains no such evidence for evolutionists' claims.

As the 500-million-year-old starfish pictured here proves, starfish have always existed as starfish, care not descended from any other life form, and never turned into any other species.

**Star Fish**
Period: Ordovician
Age: 490 to 443 million years
Location: Morocco

## Herring

**Period: Eocene**

**Age: 54 - 37 million years**

**Region: USA**

The fossil record refutes the theory of evolution in every way. The fossil herring in the picture is between 54 to 37 million years old. There is no difference between herrings that lived 54 to 37 million years ago and those living today. Examination of this 54 to 37-million-yearold fossil shows that its head, fins and tail have not altered in the least. The fact revealed by herring fossils is that life forms do not evolve, and that Almighty God created them all.

If Darwinists' claims that living things descended from one another were true, then we should encounter a large number of fossil specimens bearing the characteristics of two different life forms (such as a halfneedlefish and half-herring, or a half-whale and half-shark, or a half-trout and half-crocodile). But no such fossil has ever been found. In fact, Darwin saw that this absence of proof posed a major dilemma for him even when he first launched his theory. For that reason, he wrote the following in the chapter "Difficulties on Theory" in his book The Origin of Species:

> "Why, if species have descended from other species by insensibly fine gradations, do we not everywhere see innumerable transitional forms? Why is not all nature in confusion instead of the spec es being, as we see them, well defined? . . . But, as by this theory innumerable transitional forms must have existed, why do we not find them embedded in countless numbers in the crust of the earth?" (Charles Darwin, The Origin of Species, New York: Oxford University Press, 1998, pp. 140, 141)

Some 150 years after Darwin's time, the problem facing evolutionists is exactly the same.

**Needlefish**
Period: Cretaceous
Age : 95 million years
Location: Lebanon

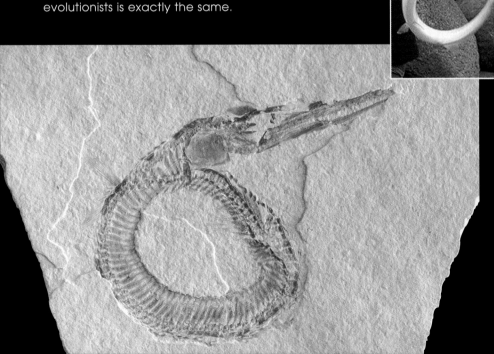

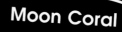

**Moon Coral**

Period: Devonian

Age: 350 million years

Region: Morocco

Trumpet Coral
(Caulastrea curvata)
Period: Jurassic
Age: 150 million years
Region: Germany

Evolutionists have never tired of making new claims over the years, yet they had to subsequently retract these claims on each and every occasion. They sometimes elected to keep fossils deliberately hidden way, and sometimes they went for imaginary reconstructions. They published the transitiona form fossils they drew using the power of their imaginations on the covers of various scientific magazines, but would later have to retract these in subsequent issues of the same publications because the fossil records unearthed subsequently demolished the evolutionists' claims, one after the other. The 350-million-year-old moon coral in the picture has never changed since the day it was first created. Just like millions of others, this fossil proves that Darwinism is merely a perverse ideology that has nothing at all to do with science.

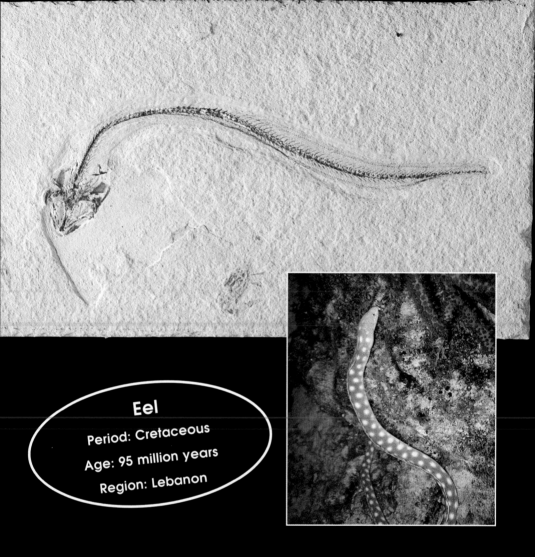

Fossils from the same species exhibit no changes throughout the time they appear in the fossil record. That fact was well-known to paleontologists even before Darwin published his Origin of Species. Darwin prophesied that subsequent generations would find new fossils to fill the gaps; but following all the paleontological research that has taken place over the last 120 years or so, it has become clear the fossil record will not confirm that prediction. Despite the passage of 95 million years, the eel in the picture has not altered in the slightest. It has never evolved or turned into any other life form.

Sea horses are very striking with their external appearance and special structures. They vary between 4 and 30 cm (1.5 to 12 inches) in length and generally live among seaweeds and other plants along coastal strips. Their protective armor keeps these animals safe from danger. That armor is so strong that it is almost impossible to break a dead sea horse with one's bare hands. The three-million-year-old sea horse in the picture says that "life forms do not evolve," and that God creates them all.

**Sea horse**
Period: Pliocene
Age: 3 million years
Region: Italy

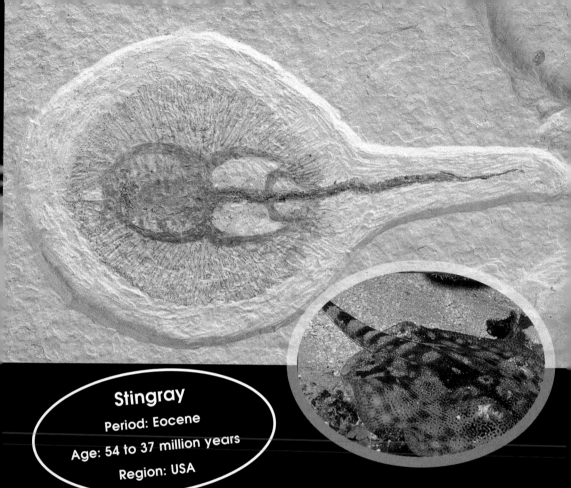

## Stingray

Period: Eocene

Age: 54 to 37 million years

Region: USA

Stingrays are cartilaginous fish. In the face of a threat, they defend themselves with the stings on their tails. Their eyes are located above their flattened bodies and their mouths are underneath. Just like sharks, they find their food by using their sense of smell and by electrical senses. They generally live submerged on the ocean floor, with only their eyes and tails discernable. The fossil pictured evidences that fish have not undergone evolution. Stingrays that lived 50 million years ago were no different from the ones living today. Despite the passage of millions of years, no change has occurred in the structure of stingrays. If evolution had really taken place, then stingrays would have undergone various stages, leaving behind many fossils documenting these sequential stages. However each fossil discovered reveal that today's stingrays and those that lived in the past are the same. All these deny the claims of evolutionists.

## Squid

**Period:** Cretaceous
**Age:** 95 million years
**Location:** Lebanon

The 95-million-year-old fossil pictured here is proof that squid have always existed as squid throughout geologic history, defying evolutionist claims. Unable to provide the slightest evidence that squid evolved from an earlier life form or developed any further, evolutionists are completely undermined by the fossil record.

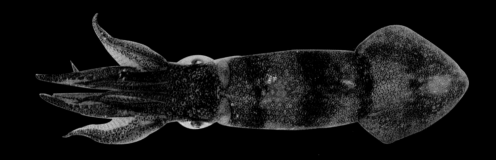

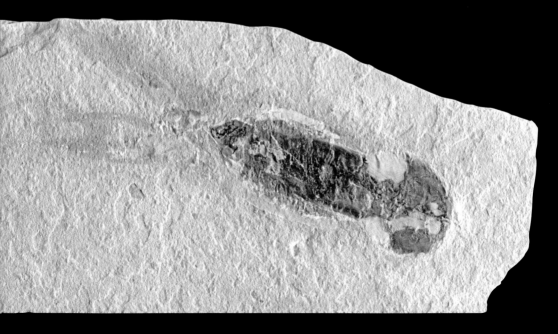

The fossil record is rich enough to permit a general comprehension of the origin of living things and provides us with a definite scenario: Various species of living creatures appeared on Earth all at once, individually and without "evolving" through any intermediate forms. This is one of the proofs that Almighty God created all living creatures. One of these fossils that demonstrates the clear fact of creation is shown here: the nearly 35-mill on-year-old remains of a crab.

**Crab**

Period: Oligocene

Age: 38-23 million years

Location: Denmark

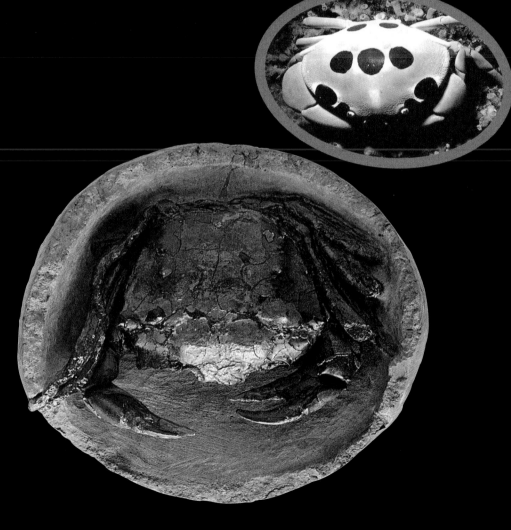

According to Darwinists' unscientific claims, plants, animals, fungi and bacteria all share a common origin. The 100 or so different animal phyla (basic taxonomic categories, such as mollusks, arthropods, worms and sponges) have all descended from one imaginary common ancestor. According to the theory, invertebrate organisms gradually (and by chance) turned into fish by acquiring a backbone; fish then turned into amphibians, amphibians into reptiles, some reptiles into birds and others into mammals. Again according to the theory, this transition encompassed a long period of time—hundreds of millions of years—and was carried forward in stages. That being the case, countless intermediate species should have emerged and existed during the long transition in question. Yet no sign of any such intermediate forms has ever been encountered in the fossil record.

Like that 95-million-year-old catshark fossil pictured here, the fossil record shows that living things came into being fully formed with all their features, and survived unchanged for millions of years.

## Catshark
Period: Cretaceous
Age: 95 million years
Location: Lebanon

**Sea Urchin**

Period: Carboniferous

Age: 295 million years

Location: USA

Pennsylvanian sea urchins are echinoderms that can be found today in all seas of the world. Sea urchi fossils dating back 300 million years reveal that these invertebrates with their complex structures have existed for millions of years. During all that time, no change have occurred in their structure, and they have undergone no intermediate stages. Darwinists are desperate when confronted by these fossils, for they prove that the evolution process has never existed.

**Soldier Fish**

Period: Cretaceous

Age: 95 million years

Location: Lebanon

The fact that soldier fish living 95 million years ago were identical to those in existence today shows that these fish have never changed over millions of years. This state of affairs, which refutes the Darwinist claim that living things evolved by changing, puts evolutionists in an impossible position. Concrete scientific findings such as the fossil record have proved that evolution never happened.

**Stingray**
Period: Cretaceous
Age: 95 million years
Location: Lebanon

Like all other fish, stingrays have always existed as stingrays. Darwinist hypotheses, claims and theses are of no scientific worth, because all the scientific data, beginning with fossil findings, refute its assertions. The hoaxes, distortions and propaganda to which Darwinists resort in order to keep their theories alive are pointless.

As the 95-million-year-old stingray pictured here shows, living things tell us that they did not evolve, but were created, and this fact is impossible to be concealed.

In The Origin of Species Revisited, Wendell R. Bird states that the theory of evolution's claim of intermediate forms is a fantasy:

> The geological record . . . tells now what it has told from the beginning, that the supposed intermediate forms between the species of different geological periods are imaginary beings, called up merely in support of a fanciful theory. (Wendell R. Bird, The Origin of Species Revisited, Thomas Nelson Inc, December 1991, p. 44)

To date, the fossil research has never produced any intermediate-form specimen to support evolutionist claims. No fossil indicating a line of descent between species has ever been unearthed. Tang fish fossils, for instance, never have any semi- or half-developed organs. No matter how far back in time one searches, every fish fossil has exactly the same characteristics as those fish living today. The 95-million-year-old tang fish fossil in the picture is just one example.

**Tang**
Period: Cretaceous
Age: 95 million years
Location: Lebanon

Starfish

Period: Silurian

Age: 430 million years

Location: Australia

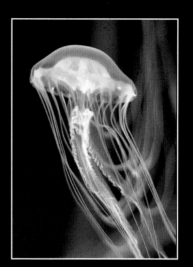

## Jellyfish

**Period:** Cambrian

**Age:** 500 million years

**Location:** USA

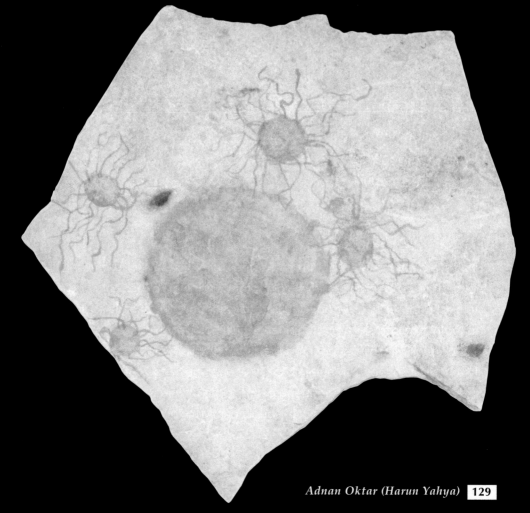

## Hatchetfish

Period: Oligocene

Age: 37 - 23 million years

Location: Czech Republic

Like several other deep sea fish these small, bright, silver fish resembling hatchets in appearance have light producing organs beneath their stomachs. These fish have up to 100 light organs capable of emitting light beneath their bodies. The hatchet fish, which has lived in the seas for millions of years with this perfect creation, never developed out of any other life form and has never turned into another one. The 37-to-23-million-year-old hatchet fish from the Oligocene period in the picture was found in the Czech Republic and is identical to specimens living today.

Like other created like forms, this 148-million-year-old opalescent squid has come down unchanged to the present day. This is obvious proof that evolution never happened and that God creates all living things. The opalescent squid is one of the decapod family, and has 10 limbs protruding from its mouth region. Opalescent squids have highly sensitive senses of smell and taste. Their eyes are so powerful that with the vision they enjoy, by means of 70 million eye cells, they can immediately recognize a danger approaching from behind and perform a series of movements to protect themselves. God has given this animal a perfect defensive system. When attacked, the opalescent squid emits a dark-colored liquid from its ink sac, thus confusing the predator and allowing it to escape at high speed.

**Opalescent Squid**

Period: Jurassic

Age: 148 million years

Location: Germany

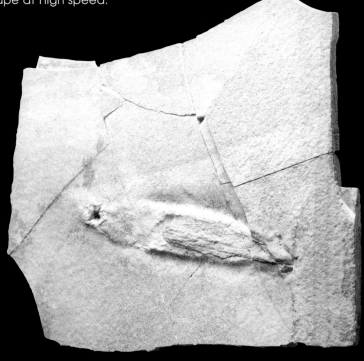

Like other created like forms, this 148-million-year-old opalescent squid has come down unchanged to the present day. This is obvious proof that evolution never happened and that God creates all living things. The opalescent squid is one of the decapod family, and has 10 limbs protruding from its mouth region. Opalescent squids have highly sensitive senses of smell and taste. Their eyes are so powerful that with the vision they enjoy, by means of 70 million eye cells, they can immediately recognize a danger approaching from behind and perform a series of movements to protect themselves. God has given this animal a perfect defensive system. When attacked, the opalescent squid emits a dark-colored liquid from its ink sac, thus confusing the predator and allowing it to escape at high speed.

Mantis shrimps, which have survived unchanged ever since the Carboniferous period (354 to 290 million years ago), are a life form that invalidates Darwinism. It is impossible to provide any evolutionary explanation for a creature that remains unaltered for 300 million years.

The mantis shrimp pictured here is 95 million years old, yet is completely identical to both those that lived 300 million years in the past and specimens alive today.

## Horn Shark

**Period:** Cretaceous
**Age:** 95 million years
**Location:** Lebanon

Present-day horn sharks have wide ridges on their long bodies. Examination of the 95-million- year-old fossil in the picture shows that the ridges on the body, and its head and tail structure have not changed in the least. The horn shark lives in the depths of the seas, and sometimes uses its pectoral fins to crawl over rocks. It lies in ambush for its prey in caves or reefs. It is approximately 1 meter long. The 95-million-year-old horn shark in the picture illustrates once again the defeat suffered by Darwinists and proves the fact that our Lord creates all living things.

## Wolf Herring

**Period: Cretaceous**
**Age: 95 million years**
**Location: Lebanon**

Because fossils demolish the claims of evolution, Darwinists usually ignore them, or else attempt to use them as tools for propaganda by means of various distortions. However, the recent exhibition of hundreds of fossils in displays, books and websites has made apparent for all to see the quandary facing evolutionists. When you can compare fossils and living specimens side by side, you have no difficulty in realizing that evolution is a lie, and need no further explanation. That is why evolutionists are in a state of panic. They are helplessly watching the global collapse of their theory, from which there can be no return. One proof of the collapse of the theory of evolution is the 95-million-year-old wolf herring fossil illustrated.

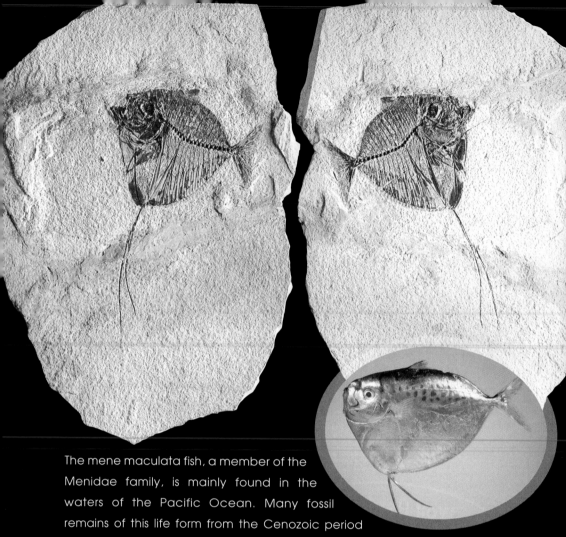

The mene maculata fish, a member of the Menidae family, is mainly found in the waters of the Pacific Ocean. Many fossil remains of this life form from the Cenozoic period (65 million years to the present) have been found. The 54 to 37-million-year-old fossil in the photograph from the Eocene period is important evidence that this life form has never changed in any way. The fossil is identical in every way to members of the species living today, with its broad body, small tail, skeletal structure and the two long fins extending from beneath its body. The fossil record literally reflects a picture of how living things were millions of years in the past. If a life form has not altered in the slightest over tens of millions of years, then it is impossible to speak of these living things evolving.

Mene Maculata
(Moonfish)

Period: Eocene

Age: 54 – 37 million years

Location: Italy

The octopus is a member of the cephalopod class. Their bodies are short and round. They have a pair of highly developed eyes. Eight arms emerge from around their heads. These arms are all of the same length and are connected to one another at the bottom by a thin membrane. There are two rows of suckers on each arm. Different species vary in size from two to three cm to 10 meters (one inch to 30 feet) in length. They move across the sea bottom by crawling along on their arms, or can also move much faster using a jet system to emit the water they absorb into their bodies at high speed. Octopi also have an advanced ability to change color, which enables them to conceal themselves with ease. They open mussel and oyster shells, place a stone inside to prevent the shell from closing again, and consume the contents.

Since they have no shells, they can flatten their bodies and arms and squeeze into very tight spaces. Like other life forms, the octopus is the work of God's magnificent creation.

with their characteristics that have gone unaltered for millions of years, horseshoe crabs, members of the family Chelicerata, are among those life forms regarded as "living fossils," even by evolutionists.

Horseshoe crabs living in the Jurassic Period, approximately 150 million years ago, are identical to those living along seacoasts today. This lack of differences demolishes evolutionist

claims and once again proves that the thesis of living things' evolution of is a ridiculous myth.

Science irrefutably reveals that living things are the work of Almighty and All-Powerful God.

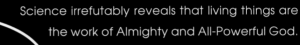

**Horseshoe Crab**
Period: Jurassic
Age: 150 million years
Location: Germany

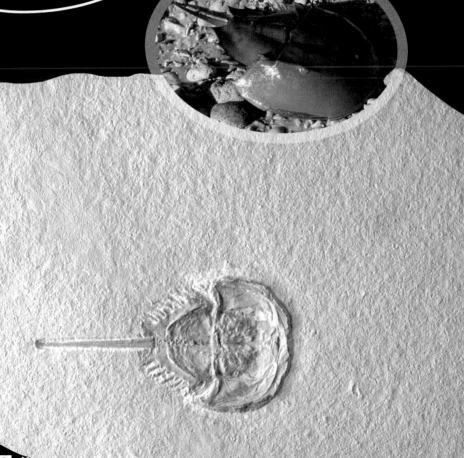

## Paddle Fish

**Period: Eocene**
**Age: 50 million years**
**Location: USA**

The paddle fish's highly pronounced spatula-like mouth, its nose structure and the small fins along most of the length of its body can be clearly seen in this 50-million-year-old fossil. The animal has never changed in the intervening 50 million years, and never evolved. When he launched his theory of evolution, Charles Darwin claimed that life forms evolved from one another by way of mutations; yet the millions of fossils that have been unearthed show that life forms are not descended from one another, and that they have remained the same since they were first created to the present day. The scientist Stephen Jay Gould states how no passage between species is possible through mutations:

"A mutation doesn't produce major new raw material (DNA). You don't make new species by mutating the species." (Stephen Jay Gould, "Is a New and General Theory of Evolution Emerging?", Lecture at Hobart & William Smith Colleges, 4 February 1980)

## Box Fish

**Period: Cretaceous**
**Age: 95 million years**
**Location: Lebanon**

You read pro-evolutionary reports in magazines and newspapers and you see similar programs and documentaries on television, not because Darwinism is a scientific viewpoint, but rather, there are tireless efforts to support it out of ideological concerns. Darwinism is the supposed scientific foundation for materialism and atheism.

No one who accepts Darwinism's invalidity can support materialism and atheism. That is why, despite all scientific findings and evidence arguing against the theory of evolution, these facts are ignored, and Darwinism continues to be defended through lies and distortions.

One of the proofs that evolutionists refuse to acknowledge are the fossils, now numbering in the millions, each one of them clear proof of Creation. Like the 95-million-year-old box fish pictured, all fossils tell us that living things never evolved, and that God created them all.

Another scientific discovery showing that there was no process of evolution, as the Darwinists claim, is the fossilized shrimp illustrated here. Since shrimp first came into existence, they have always displayed all the same organs and characteristics as they have today and have undergone no changes in all that time. This shrimp fossil shows plainly that evolution is an imaginary scenario.

**Shrimp**
Period: Jurassique
Age: 208 - 146 million years
Location: Germany

**Bowfin**

Period: Eocene

Age: 50 million years

Location: Germany

Bowfins belong to the the Amiidae family. As with many other fish species, they possess a rich fossil history. One of the earliest known fossil specimens is around 150 million years old.

All the fossils obtained show that bo fins have been exactly the same for millions of ears, and have never evolved in any way. There is no difference between the 50-million-year-old bowfin pictured and those alive today.

## Capros

**Period: Oligocene**

**Age: 35 million years**

**Location: Poland**

The fact that a Capros living 35 millions years ago is identical to specimens alive today is one of the most significant proofs that evolution is a
terrible falsehood. Not a single fossil representing evidence for evolution
has ever been found during 150 years of paleontological excavations.
All the fossils unearthed show that living things never evolved.

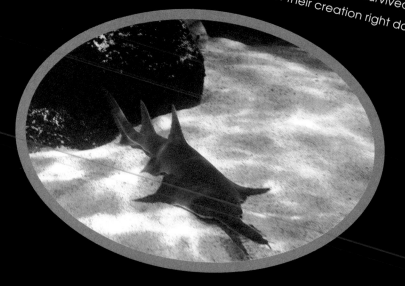

## Sawfish

**Period:** Cretaceous

**Age:** 95 million years

**Location:** Lebanon

There are no differences between present-day specimens and the 95-million-year-old sawfish pictured. This, by itself, puts the theory of evolution in a severe quandary. Our Almighty Lord has created all living things as separate species, which have survived unchanged from the moment of their creation right down to today.

## Catshark

**Period: Cretaceous**
**Age: 95 million years**
**Location: Lebanon**

Cat sharks that lived millions of years ago possessed all the same fully formed features as those living today— as is confirmed by the 95-million-year-old cat shark pictured, which is identical to present-day specimens. God has created cat shark to be fully formed and with nothing lacking, as He has all other living things. Like them, cat sharks never underwent evolution.

*Adnan Oktar (Harun Yahya)*

## Sturgeon
**Period: Cretaceous**
**Age: 144-65 million years**
**Location: China**

The sturgeons, of which only two families remain in existence, have always been sturgeons. They have neither developed from, nor turned into any other species. Fossil finds corroborate the fact that like all other creatures, sturgeons have never undergone any process of evolution.

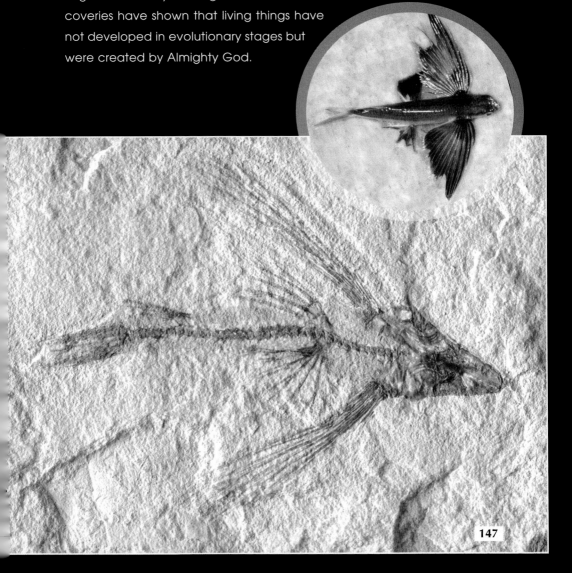

## Flying Fish
**Period: Cretaceous**
**Age: 95 million years**
**Location: Lebanon**

Flying fish leap out of the water, propelled by rapid movements of their tail fin and glide a certain distance before gently dropping back into the water. During this airborne movement, the fish can reach a speed of 50 kilometers (31 miles) an hour. There is no difference between flying fish living today and those that lived about 100 million years ago. The species has not undergone the slightest change in all that time, which destroys all the claims of the evolutionists about the origins and history of living creatures. Scientific discoveries have shown that living things have not developed in evolutionary stages but were created by Almighty God.

147

# Fossil Specimens of Plants

**Willow**

Period: Eocene

Age: 54-37 million years

Location: USA

## Pine Cone

**Period: Early Tertiary**

**Age: 65-23 million years**

**Location: Germany**

The structure of cones, organs on conifers that contain the plant's ovaries, has remained the same for millions of years, as with the structures of all other living species. This cone, 65 to 23 million years old, and identical ones of our day are one of the important examples revealing that throughout these long ages, evolution has never occurred.

## Magnolia Leaf

**Period: Eocene**
**Age: 50 million years**
**Location: Canada**

Magnolia trees, with green leaves that do not fall in winter and with their delightful scent, have never changed and continue to be one of the Earth's loveliest adornments.

Had evolution really taken place, which it definitely did not, then life forms should appear gradually with small changes and should also continue to change. However, the fossil record shows the exact opposite. Different living classes appeared suddenlyin the fossil record, with no ancestors behind them, and have remained in a state of stasis for hundreds of millions of years.

God created all living things. Fossil specimens dating back millions of years reveal this fact once again in the most flawless way. God is the sublime and almighty Creator of all things.

# Sycamore Ranch with Seed Pods

**Period: Oligocene**

**Age: 38-23 million years**

**Location: USA**

Evolutionists claim that plants originated from a common ancestor, yet they fail to offer a single scientific finding to prove it.

On the other hand, innumerable findings show that plants were separately created, with features distinct to each species, and that they did not evolve. One of these is the 38- to 23-millionyear- old sycamore branch that fossilized together with its seed pods. This fossil, which is no different from the sycamores alive today, invalidates the theory of evolution.

**Redbud Leaf**

Period: Eocene

Age: 50 million years

Location: Canada

In terms of both general structure, and also when examined microbiologically, leaves can be seen to have highly detailed and complex systems planned in every way in order to provide the greatest energy production possible. In order to be able to manufacture energy, the leaf needs to receive heat and carbon dioxide from the external environment. All the structures in leaves are arranged in order that these two elements can easily be obtained. For example, leaves have broad surfaces and this facilitates the exchanges of gas necessary for photosynthesis (processes such as the absorption of carbon dioxide and the emission of oxygen).

All plant leaves have had these features since the moment they first came into being and none has ever acquired them as the result of blind chance. God has created them with great wisdom, together with their wondrous properties.

**Ginkgo Leaf**

Period: Eocene

Age: 50 million years

Location: Canada

The theory of evolution cannot explain the origins of living organisms and is also desperate in the face of fossil ginkgo leaves, showing that the species has remained unchanged for tens of millions of years. Such fossils, proving that living organisms have stayed the same as long as they've existed, have dealt a fatal blow to the theory of evolution. As many other branches of science, paleontology also confirms that Creation is an obvious fact.

For the last 150 years, every corner of the Earth has been excavated in search of fossils, and millions of them have been discovered. But among all these fossils, there exists not a single half-developed specimen that possesses the features of two different living species—which can be termed an intermediate "missing link." Every fossil discovered so far reveals that living beings emerged all of a sudden and have never changed, as long as they did not become extinct. This has a clear implication: God created living beings.

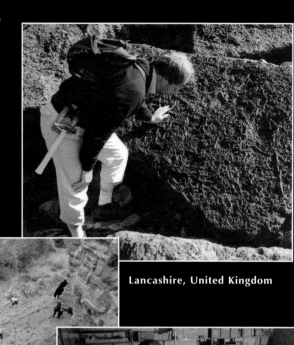

Lancashire, United Kingdom

Green River Formation, USA

Throughout history, turtles have remained as turtles, gnats have remained as gnats, ants have remained as ants and ginkgo leaves remained as ginkgo leaves. No matter how old a fossil ginkgo leaf we examine is, we see that it has the very same structure of today's ginkgos. The leaves are the very same, whether 50 million years old or hundreds of millions of years old. Like all other living things, the ginkgo has not undergone any changes and has not lived through any process of evolution. Each species is created in the same way with the superior artistry of our Lord.

**Ginkgo Leaf**

Period: Eocene

Age: 54-37 million years

Location: Canada

# Fern

**Period:** Carboniferous

**Age:** 320 million years

**Location:** United Kingdom

The fossil pictured is evidence that ferns did not evolve from other plants, and have not transformed into ferns of our day by gradual changes. They have always remained as ferns, with all their features and functions. This fossil, 320 million years old, is evidence that as with all living and non-living things, Almighty God created plants; and that evolution is nothing but a scenario based on a figment of imagination.

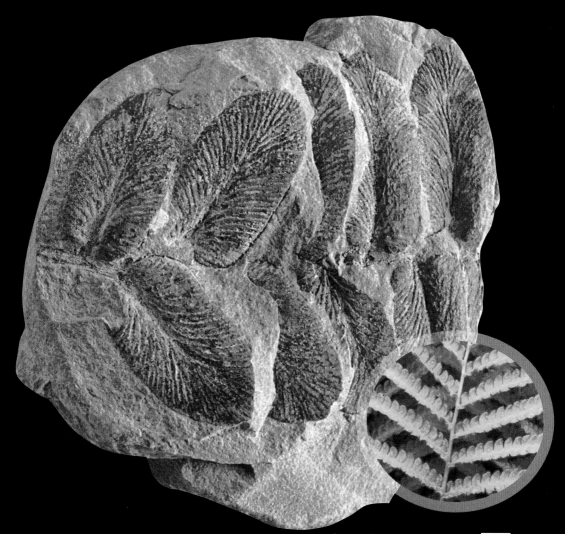

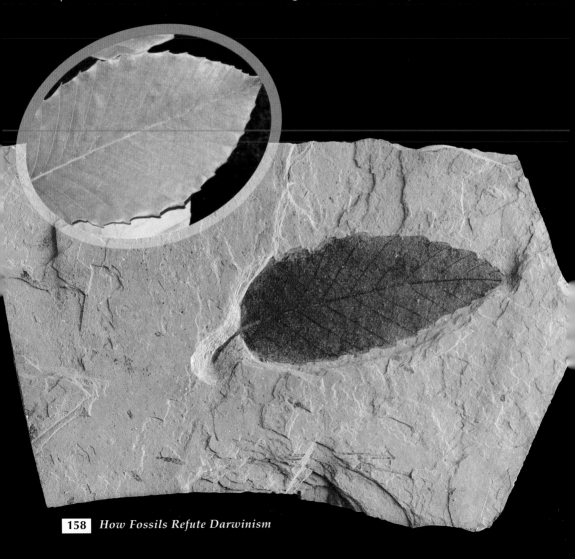

## Beech Leaf

**Period:** Eocene

**Age:** 50 million years

**Location:** Canada

Despite all the research and enormous labor and means expended over the last 150 years, no findings of any kind have been unearthed that might support the theory of evolution. If such a thing as evolution had in fact taken place, then countless proofs have been discovered by now. Indeed, many scientists since Darwin's day have admitted there should be a large quantity of evidence, but that it has never been found.

On the other hand, countless findings and proofs reveal that Creation is a manifest truth. One of these is the fossil specimen pictured here, which proves that beech leafs have not changed over 50 million years.

**Sequoia Leaf**

Period: Eocene

Age: 50 million years

Location: Canada

Countless remains of sequoia leaves that have survived as fossils prove that this plant has survived in different places on Earth and has never changed. Thanks to this important evidence, Darwinist speculations about the imaginary evolution of plants no longer exist. This 50-million-year-old sequoia leaf is one of the proofs that puts an end to these speculations.

## Serviceberry Leaf

Period: Eocene

Age: 50 million years

Location: Canada

Like all other living organisms, plants too emerged in the fossil record quite suddenly and withbstructures peculiar to them. The appearance and structures they displayed millions of years ago is the same as the appearance and structures they do now. This shows that living things are created by One having a superior wisdom, that is, our Lord, God. One piece of evidence is this serviceberry leaf, about 50 million years old.

**Horsechestnut Leaves**

Period: Paleocene

Age: 58 million years

Location: USA

One of the fossils revealing that Darwin was wrong is this 58-million-year-old fossilized horsechestnut leaf.

## Hackberry Leaf

**Period: Eocene**

**Age: 45 million years**

**Location: USA**

Celtis or hackberry, is a genus of 60 to 70 deciduous trees widespread in East Asia, South and Middle North America. They are generally medium-sized trees, reaching a height of 10 to 25 meters (33 to 82 feet).

Like all other plants, hackberries have always remained as hackberries, as is testified by the fossil record. All hackberry fossils unearthed to date reveal that the hackberries of today are identical with those that lived tens of millions of years ago. This exact similarityrefutes the theory of evolution.

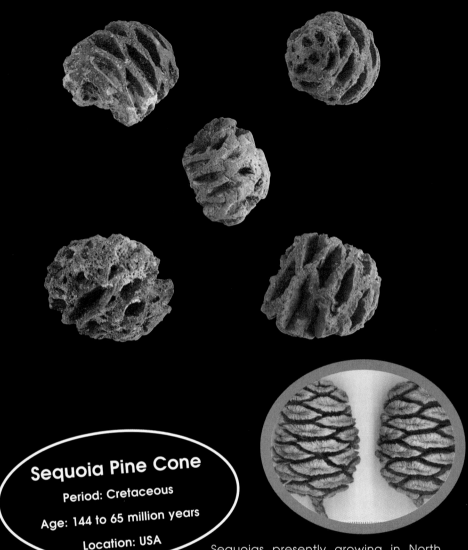

**Sequoia Pine Cone**

Period: Cretaceous

Age: 144 to 65 million years

Location: USA

Sequoias presently growing in North America can reach more than 100 meters in height; there are countless fossil specimens showing that these trees' foliage has remained the same for tens of millions of years. The fossil in the picture is around 140 million years old. These specimens once again condemn evolutionists, who cannot explain scientifically how plants first emerged and why there is such a variety of them, to a profound silence.

It is clear that each species of plant which appears suddenly in the fossil record, together with its own unique features and which has survived completely unchanged for millions of years, has been created by Almighty God.

## Elm Leaf

Period: Eocene

Age : 50 million years

Location: USA

The elm trees that grow in temperate climates are generally found in North America, Europe and Asia. 50-million-year-old fossil elm tree leaves clearly refute the claims of the evolution of plants.

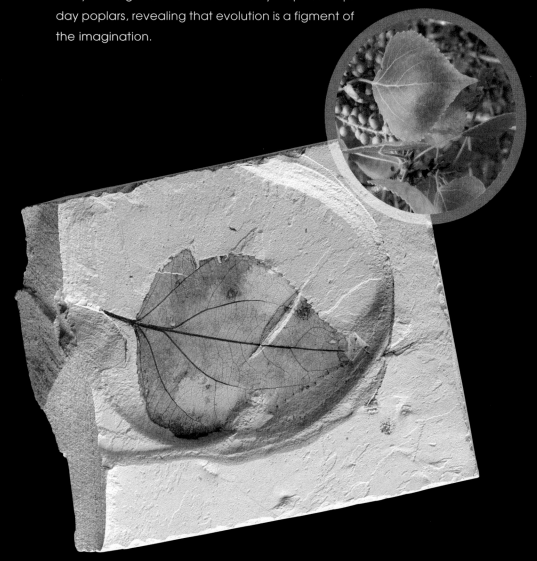

## Poplar Leaf

**Period:** Eocene

**Age:** 54 to 37 million years

**Location:** USA

This fossil—which proves that poplars are not descended from any other plant, that they have no evolutionary forerunner and have always existed as poplars—is a proof of Creation. Poplars that lived around 50 million years ago are identical in every respect to present-day poplars, revealing that evolution is a figment of the imagination.

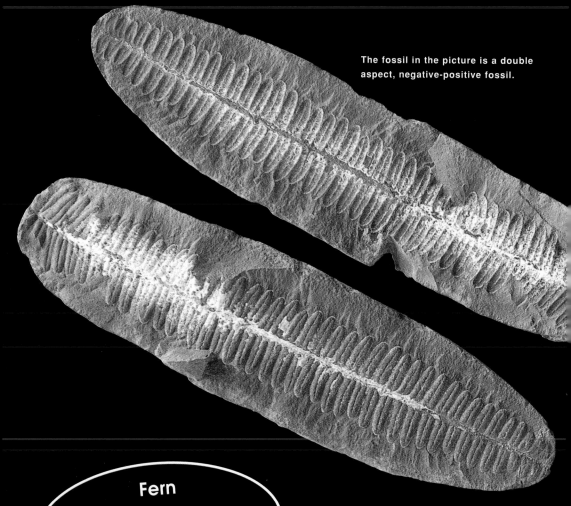

The fossil in the picture is a double aspect, negative-positive fossil.

### Fern

**Period: Carboniferous**

**Age: 300 million years**

**Location: USA**

Paleontological findings prove that ferns, like all other living things, did not emerge by way of evolution and that, on the contrary, they were created.

Many contemporary scientists accept that the fossil record supports Creation rather than evolution, and that intermediate life forms exist only in evolutionists' imaginations.

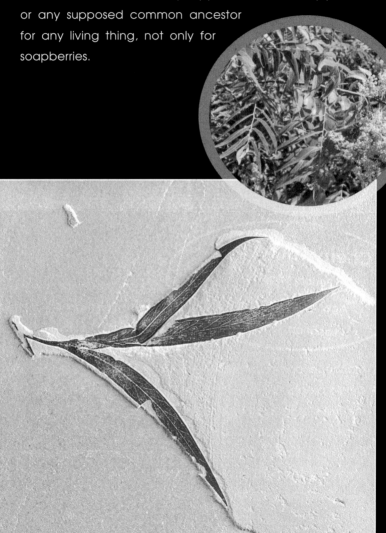

**Soapberry Leaf**

Period: Cretaceous

Age: 95 million years

Location: Lebanon

No fossil unearthed to date shows that soapberry leaves ever underwent evolution.

All soapberry fossils have exactly the same characteristics as those living today. Evolutionists are unable to indicate any supposed evolutionary process or any supposed common ancestor for any living thing, not only for soapberries.

**Myrica Leaf**

Period: Oligocene

Age : 30 million years

Location: France

Rather than debate the meaning of scientific findings, Darwinists prefer to resort to psychological propaganda techniques, to restrict freedom of thought by banning works that refute evolution, and to influence the public by adopting a mocking style. They usually employ psychological warfare techniques for that purpose.

Evolutionists should not turn a deaf ear to others and resort to slander, insult and flase accusations without even a glance at the available evidence and documentation. If they are truly confident in their theory and possess scientific evidence, they should display it to silence their opposition on an intellectual level. However, they have never yet done so, and it is impossible for them to do so, because Darwinists have not a single piece of evidence to support their theory.

## Soapberry Leaf

**Period:** Cretaceous
**Age:** 95 million years
**Location:** Lebanon

No fossil unearthed to date shows that soapberry leaves ever underwent evolution.

All soapberry fossils have exactly the same characteristics as those living today. Evolutionists are unable to indicate any supposed evolutionary process or any supposed common ancestor for any living thing, not only for soapberries.

## Cherry Laurel Leaf

**Period: Eocene**

**Age: 50 million years**

**Location: Canada**

Cherry laurel trees in the past lived in the same manner as today's. Were Darwinists telling the truth, then present-day cherry laurel trees should bear no resemblance, or only a partial one, to those of the past. In addition, other fossils should be able to show how the cherry laurel trees of the past turned into the trees of today. But over the last two centuries or so, Darwinists have been unable to obtain any evidence of this process, which exists solely in their imaginations. All the findings made reveal that cherry laurels have always existed as cherry laurels, that they have not evolved, and that they were therefore created.

## Sassafras Leaf

**Period: Eocene**

**Age: 54-37 million years**

**Location: Canada**

One of the most familiar forms of Darwinist propaganda are groundless slogans along the lines of "Rejection of the theory of evolution is a dogma," or "Denying the theory of evolution is unscientific." In fact, however, such statements are preconceptions based on evolutionists' biased conception of science. "Science," according to the Darwinist definition, is not a discipline that researches, investigates and analyses its findings in a neutral manner and then accepts the results of those findings. According to Darwinists, scientific inquiries must first confirm their own beliefs and ideas and in the process, which findings must be interpreted by distorting them in line with evolutionist dogma.

**Myrica Leaf**

Period: Oligocene

Age : 30 million years

Location: France

Rather than debate the meaning of scientific findings, Darwinists prefer to resort to psychological propaganda techniques, to restrict freedom of thought by banning works that refute evolution, and to influence the public by adopting a mocking style. They usually employ psychological warfare techniques for that purpose.

Evolutionists should not turn a deaf ear to others and resort to slander, insult and flase accusations without even a glance at the available evidence and documentation. If they are truly confident in their theory and possess scientific evidence, they should display it to silence their opposition on an intellectual level. However, they have never yet done so, and it is impossible for them to do so, because Darwinists have not a single piece of evidence to support their theory.

## Katsura Tree Leaf

**Period: Paleocene**

**Age: 58 million years**

**Location: USA**

All the structures possessed by leaves are of vital importance. Flawlessly functioning systems like those in existence today need to be present all together for a plant to live and reproduce. These structures cannot, therefore, come into being gradually. All the fossil plants that have been found confirm that they have had the same perfect structures since plants first appeared on Earth. One of these is the 85- million-year-old katsura tree leaf, shown in the picture, which has come down to the present day with all its details preserved.

**Honeysuckle Leaf**

Period: Paleocene

Age: 58 million years

Location: USA

The absence of any differences between the 58-million-year-old honeysuckle leaf pictured here and those alive today is a sufficient response by itself to evolutionist claims. One of the major predicaments that confronts scientists espousing the scenario of plant evolution is the lack of even a single intermediate-form fossil. There are no "primitive" plant fossils with half-developed systems. To date, no evidence has been produced that one plant is the ancestor of any other. Therefore, family trees purporting to show the supposed evolution of plants are entirely imaginary, with no scientific basis to them at all.

In his article The Evolution of Flowering Plants, the paleobotanist Daniel Axelrod makes the following comment on the origin of flowering plants:

"The ancestral group that gave rise to angiosperms has not yet been identified in the fossil record, and no living angiosperm points to such an ancestral alliance." (D. I. Axelrod, "The Evolution of Flowering Plants," in Evolution After Darwin: Vol. 1: The Evolution of Life, ed. S. Tax, Chicago, IL: University of Chicago Press, 1960, pp. 264-274)

As you can see from his admission, fossil research over the last 150 years or so has failed to produce even a single fossil that can be construed as the ancestor of flowering plants. This refutes the Darwinist claim that plants descended from one another by undergoing very small changes over very lengthy periods of time.

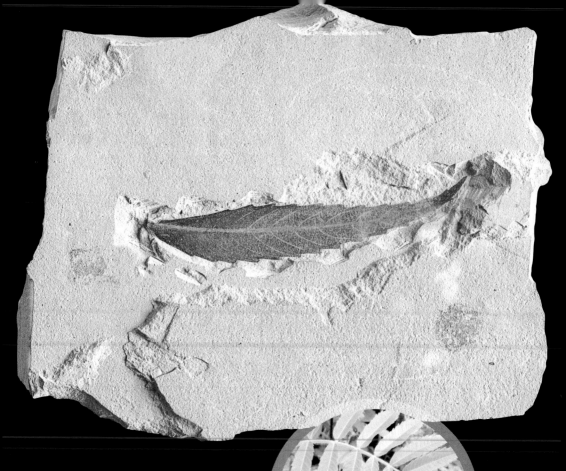

**Sumac Leaf**

Period: Eocene

Age: 45 million years

Location: USA

Plants have been making photosynthesis in the same way they do today for millions of years. They possessed hydraulic systems powerful enough to crack concrete, pumps that can raise water absorbed from the soil many meters in height and chemical factories that manufacture food for living things. Plants were created hundreds of millions of years ago.

## Auracarian Cone

**Period:** Cretaceous

**Age:** 125 million years

**Location:** Brazil

A huge number of very different species are living on the Earth. These life forms are equipped with ever more complex features that totally do away with Darwinism.

Darwinists are totally unable to account for this; flawless fossils of these living things that have survived millions of years down to the present day leave them literally speechless.

Fossils of living things that lived millions of years in the past show that living things never evolved and that the theory of evolution is devoid of any supporting evidence and a totally invalid theory. With their complex equipment and characteristics unique to their own species, living things that lived millions of years ago, and those living today, are all miracles created by God.

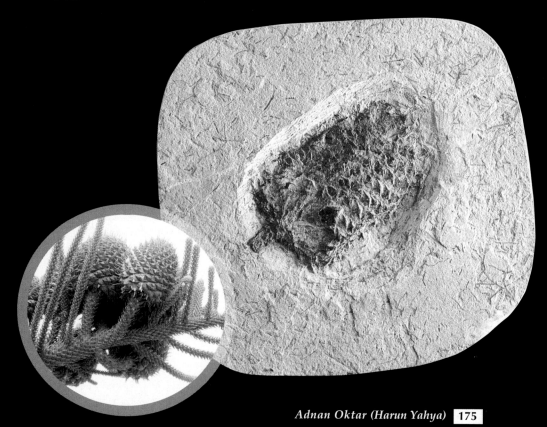

**Turkey Oak Leaf**

Period: Pliocene

Age: 5.1 - 1.8 million years

Location: Bulgaria

Plants are magnificent life forms, with photosynthesis systems that turn light into food and that constantly produce energy and oxygen, with mechanisms that cleanse nature and establish an ecological balance and aesthetic proper-ties that speak to human beings, such as taste, smell and color.

Today only some 10,000 species of plants, which have matchless systems for very beneficial purposes, have been studied; however, that research has shown that every plant possesses the most amazing features of creation.

Evolutionists simply have no logical and scientific response to the question of howplants first appeared. As with other matters, the only account they can come up with for the existence of plants is purely imaginary scenarios. It is Almighty God, the Creator of the Earth and sky and all that lies between, Who creates plants.

**Palm Leaf**
Period: Eocene
Age: 50 million years
Location: USA

Fossil research over the last 150 years has shown that the hopes of Darwin and the evolutionists who followed him were all in vain, and not a single transitional form fossil has ever been found.

Today there are some 450 million fossils in thousands of museums and collections. All these fossils belong to species with their own unique characteristics, and that are completely distinct from one another. None of the half-fish, half-amphibian, or halfdinosaur, half-bird, or half-monkey, half-human and similar life forms that evolutionists sought with great expectations have ever been encountered. All the fossils unearthed, such as the palm leaf fossil in the picture, are findings that refute evolution.

## Walnut

**Period: Pliocene**

**Age: 2.5 million years**

**Location: Holland**

There are different types of walnut tree growing almost everywhere in the world. The fossil walnuts you see here have never changed over millions of years, and have remained exactly the same since the moment they were first created.

## Diospyros

**Period: Eocene**

**Age: 40 million years**

**Location: France**

According to Darwinists' unscientific claims, date trees, pine trees, cacti, orchids, carnations, roses, cherry trees, grasses, ferns—in short, all plants share the same imaginary forebear. But when asked about the nature of this common forebear, or by what stages different plants diverged from one another and finally assumed their present forms, evolutionists have no scientic response to give.

## Persea Leaf

**Period: Eocene**

**Age: 50 million years**

**Location: USA**

The avocado is the best known member of this plant family of 150 species, whose leaves never fall. This 50-million-yearold fossil persea leaf is exactly the same as those living today. Neither animals nor plants gradually changed. They never evolved. God created all living things.

There is not the slightest difference between horsetail that existed some 200 million years ago and those living today. If a living thing has preserved its entire structure for 200 millionyears, without undergoing the slightest change, then it is impossible to speak of it having evolved. That impossibility applies to all life forms and species. Fossils, which document history of life, refute evolution.

**Horsetail**

Period: Triassic

Age: 248 to 206 million years

Location: Australia

## Pine

**Period:** Miocene

**Age:** 23 - 5 million years

**Location:** USA

Pines are coniferous, cone-bearing trees. Evolutionists maintain that life forms descended from a common ancestor and turned into different species by undergoing gradual and minute changes. That claim is devoid of any scientific evidence. The fossil record clearly shows that life forms never changed and survived exactly as they were first created. The Miocene Period fossil pine in the picture is one piece of evidence that proves that. Pines have come down to us today unchanged for millions of years.

## Distylium Leaf

**Period: Eocene**

**Age: 50 million years**

**Location: USA**

These plants, members of the family Hamamelidaceae, comprise 18 different species and are one of the millions of life forms in the fossil record. Looking at the 50-million-year-old fossil distylium leaf in the picture, it is strikingly identical to specimens living today. If evolutionists' claims were true, then these plants should have undergone various changes over the last 50 million years; but this fossil alone is evidence that refutes Darwinism. The layers of the Earth are full of millions of similar fossils that all confirm creation.

# FOSSIL SPECIMENS
# OF LAND ANIMALS

**Lion Skull**

Period: Cetaceous

Age: 82 million years

Location: China

**Crocodile**

Period: Cretaceous

Age: 65 million years

Location: China

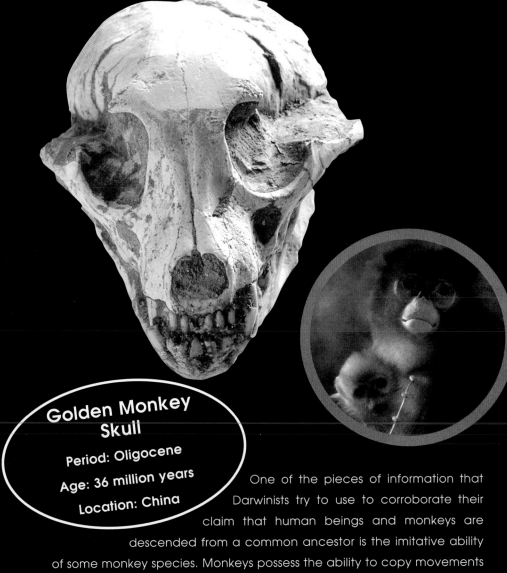

**Golden Monkey Skull**

Period: Oligocene

Age: 36 million years

Location: China

One of the pieces of information that Darwinists try to use to corroborate their claim that human beings and monkeys are descended from a common ancestor is the imitative ability of some monkey species. Monkeys possess the ability to copy movements and behavior they see around them. But this does not enable them one day to turn into human beings. If that were so, then other well-known species should also gradually turn into humans. In addition to monkeys, parrots, for example, also possess the ability to imitate speech. Therefore, according to the Darwinists illogical claims, there should be a high probability of parrots turning into human beings.

Countless findings, like the 36-million-year-old golden monkey skull in the picture, prove that living things have always remained the same and never changed and turned into any other life form, and it is quite pointless to persist with illogical evolutionist claims.

Wolverine Skull

Period: Cretaceous

Age: 90 million years

Location: China

Many Darwinists have led academic careers, read dozens of books, carried out countless pieces of research, and published many scientific papers. It is astonishing that they are still unable to see the most obvious truths. They are quite unable to understand, for instance, that the "living fossils"—living organisms that have never undergone the slightest change over the course of millions of years—represent a concrete refutation of Darwinism. They cannot bring themselves to admit the absence of any of the supposed "intermediate-form fossils" they need to confirm their theories.

Despite Darwinists' difficulties in admitting this truth, countless fossils such as the 90-million-year-old skull in the picture all demonstrate that evolution never occurred.

**Zebra Skull**
Period: Eocene
Age: 45 million years
Location: China

God has created all living things with their different appearances and forms. In the same way that their lifestyles and needs differ, so there are profound differences in their body structures. This means it is not difficult to describe the fossils that are unearthed, making it possible to establish the anatomical features of a living thing whose fossil remains have been discovered. The 45-million-year-old zebra fossil illustrated makes this distinction. It's evident that there is no difference between the fossil's characteristics and those of a present-day zebra's skull.

There is no doubt that this is one of God's divine miracles. The scientific evidence to hand is too definitive for scientists to be able to deny, even if they are evolutionists. It's a scientific fact that species have not changed, and they have undergone no evolutionary process.

The history of evolution is filled with hoaxes. Attempts have been made to portray fossils of various extinct life forms or even a few fragments of fossilized bone as evidence of imaginary transitions. Fossils of living species have long been described to the public by the evolutionists as living things that have been evolving. But a profound silence has now replaced all this misleading speculation regarding fossils. Eventually, as you can see from the 73-million-year-old hyena skull shown here, it was realized that many present-day life forms lived millions of years ago in exactly the same forms they have now and that therefore, they never evolved. The time has now come for evolutionists to put an end to their hoaxes and speculations about the myth of human evolution.

**Hyena Skull**
Period: Cretaceous
Age: 73 million years
Location: China

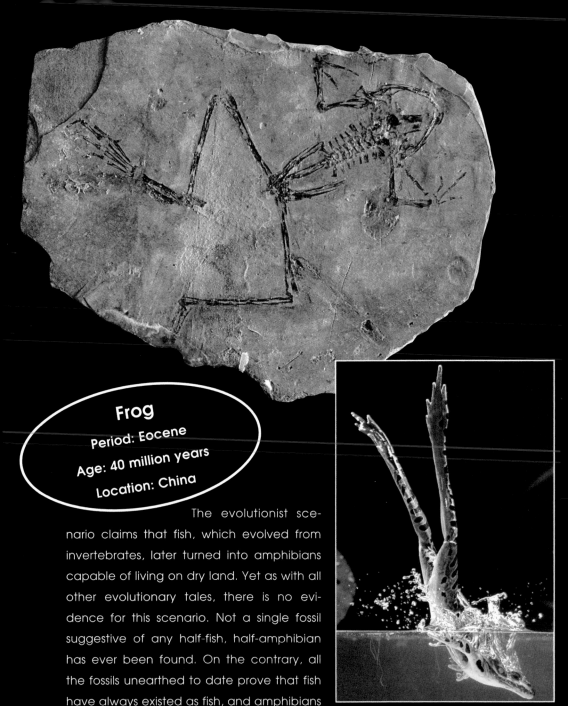

## Frog

Period: Eocene

Age: 40 million years

Location: China

The evolutionist scenario claims that fish, which evolved from invertebrates, later turned into amphibians capable of living on dry land. Yet as with all other evolutionary tales, there is no evidence for this scenario. Not a single fossil suggestive of any half-fish, half-amphibian has ever been found. On the contrary, all the fossils unearthed to date prove that fish have always existed as fish, and amphibians as amphibians.

The 40-million-year-old frog fossil pictured proves that frogs have never altered in all that time— in other words, that they never evolved.

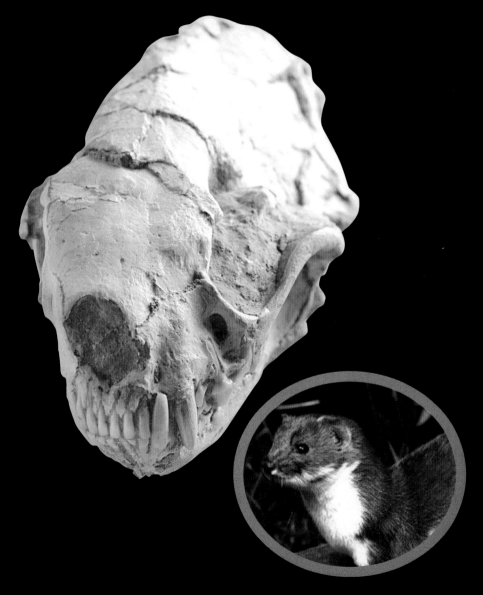

## Weasel Skull

**Period:** Miocene

**Age:** 23 to 5 million years

**Location:** China

Weasels, members of the family Mustelidae, are another life form that, with their structures that have remained unchanged for millions of years, refutes the claims of evolution.

## Crocodile

**Period:** Cretaceous
**Age:** 65 million years
**Location:** China

Darwinists maintain that marine life forms represent the ancestors of reptiles. According to this claim—which is uncorroborated by any scientific finding—fish left stranded without water were one day forced to emerge onto dry land, thus giving rise to reptiles. Yet not one single fossilized half-fish, half-reptile to support this scenario has ever been encountered. Among all the hundreds of thousands of fossils found so far, fish always appear as distinct fish, and reptiles as obvious reptiles.

Every fossil discovered is identical to its counterparts alive today, or else belongs to a species that once existed, but has become extinct. One example is the 65-million-year-old fossil crocodile pictured, a proof that crocodiles have always existed as crocodiles.

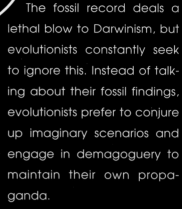

## Antelope Skull

**Period: Cretaceous**
**Age: 83 million years**
**Location: China**

The fossil record deals a lethal blow to Darwinism, but evolutionists constantly seek to ignore this. Instead of talking about their fossil findings, evolutionists prefer to conjure up imaginary scenarios and engage in demagoguery to maintain their own propaganda.

Yet no matter how much evolutionists flee from the facts, millions of fossils like the 83-million-year-old antelope skull pictured proclaim that evolution never happened.

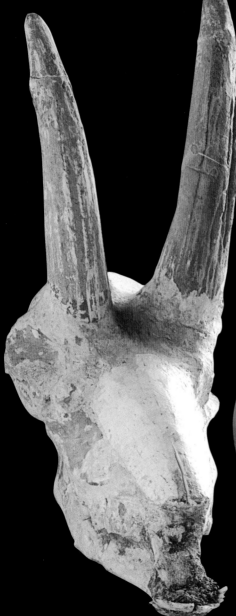

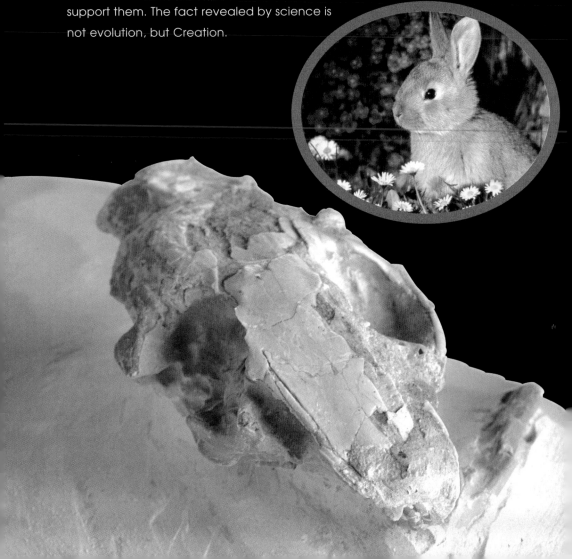

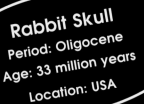

**Rabbit Skull**
Period: Oligocene
Age: 33 million years
Location: USA

If Darwinists' claims were true, then an odd-looking rabbit fossil with a skull as yet partly developed, with only half ears and a half jaw, should have been found in the excavations carried out so far. But no such semi-developed rabbit fossil has ever been seen. Every rabbit fossil discovered has fully formed, and flawless characteristics, just like the 33-million-year fossil pictured. That being the case, it is meaningless for Darwinists to persist in their claims, since the fossil findings do not support them. The fact revealed by science is not evolution, but Creation.

Darwin imagined that living things changed slowly. In his view, all living things, humans included, were descended from other species and thus arrived at their modern-day appearances. Given that 19th-century science provided no evidence to support his hypothesis, Darwin believed that the intermediate-form fossils that should exist would be found at a later date. One fossil that proves that its species never passed through any intermediate stages is the 32-million-year-old Tasmanian devil skull pictured here.

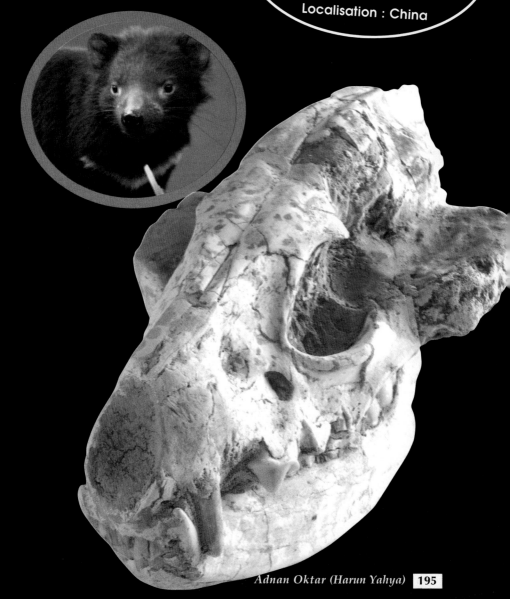

**Tasmanian Devil Skull**

Period: Oligocene

Age: 32 million years

Localisation : China

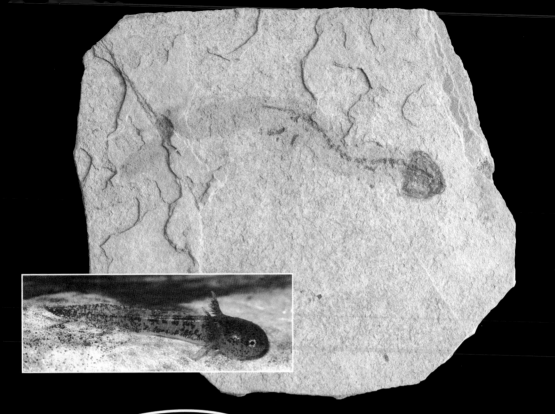

Evolutionists claim that fish are the supposed forerunners of amphibians like the salamander, even though they are completely unable to substantiate those claims.

No matter which species of fish evolutionists may choose to regard as the supposed forebear of amphibians, an enormous number of changes would be needed in order for that fish to be able to transform itself into an amphibian. Therefore, there should be an equally vast number of intermediate forms between the two: There must have been odd-looking creatures with half-formed feet and halffins, with both half-gills and half-developed lungs, or with semi-developed kidneys etc, numbering in the millions.

However, not a single one has ever been encountered in the fossil record. Among the countless fossils in existence, there are fully formed fish and fully formed amphibians, but no intermediate forms. This is something that evolutionists do admit from time to time, even though it totally refutes their theory.

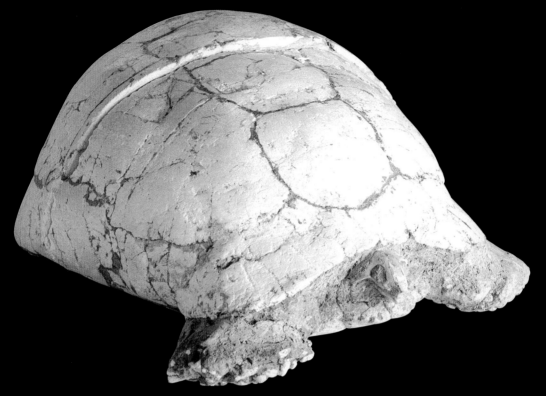

## Turtle

Period: Cretaceous

Age: 98 million years old

Location: China

Darwinists, who maintain that living species are descended from another and develop by constant small changes, are at a loss to explain the stasis, or total stability, observed within those same species. The theory of evolution, which maintains that human beings are descended from apes, must explain why no other life forms underwent the imaginary transition similar to the one from ape to human. Evolutionists have no rational and logical answer to give. Birds never changed. Rhinoceroses, foxes and hyenas never changed; and neither did the 98-million-year old turtle shown here.

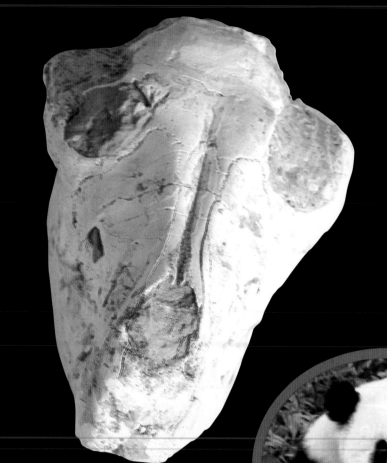

Pandas, which feed solely on bamboo shoots, are members of the family Ailuridae. Their homeland is the western regions of China. Pandas that lived 96 million years ago have all the features of present-day pandas. This fact, proved by fossils and which refute evolution, is plainly obvious for anyone to see. The fact that Darwinists insist on ignoring the evidence changes nothing. Living things did not emerge as the result of any evolutionary process. All things, living or otherwise, are created by God.

**Panda Skull**

Period: Cretaceous

Age: 96 million years

Location: China

The perfect detail in this 51-million-year-old red wolf skull in the picture accurately reflects the features of this life form.

Had no such fossil emerged, Darwinists would have most definitely continued to fabricate countless scenarios about the supposed evolution of red wolves. They would be proposing countless false intermediate forms and telling countless fictions.

But this fossil specimen puts an end to Darwinist myths. This also applies to all other life forms and also to man. Every scenario produced by Darwinists is completely based on lies, and that is a fact now agreed on by everyone.

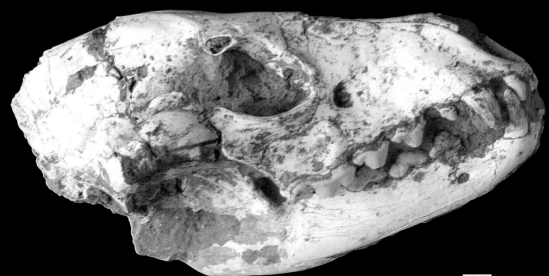

**Snake**

Period: Eocene

Age: 50 million years

Location: Germany

One thing that evolutionists are at a loss to explain is the origin of reptiles. Between the various classes of reptiles, such as snakes, alligators, turtles and lizards, there are strict boundaries. The fossil record shows that each of these categories has come into existence at once, with very different physical characteristics. One of these proofs to deny that reptiles underwentevolution is the 50-million-year-old snake fossil shown in the picture.

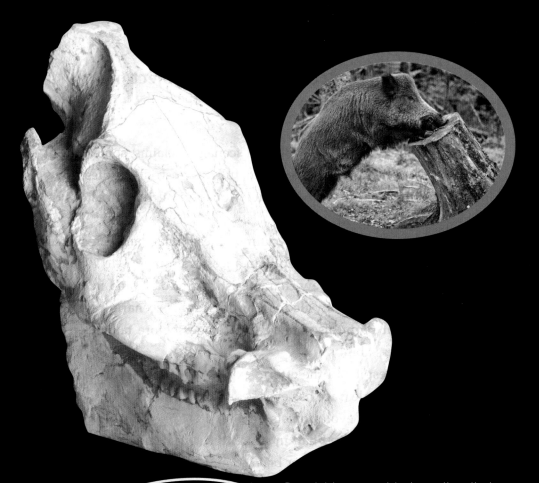

**Boar Skull**
Period: Paleocene
Age: 58 million years
Location: China

Darwinists were able to gather their original supporters by using a very primitive logic. In a climate of scientific ignorance, it was easy to convince the public that proteins and eventually, cells could form spontaneously from muddy water that mammals hunting in water eventually developed fins and turned into dolphins and thatmonkeys decided to stop leaping from tree to tree and instead to walk upright, and thus evolved into human beings.

The sciences of genetics and paleontology were unknown, so all these imaginary transitions were depicted as incontrovertible fact. But now Darwinists are in a far more difficult position. The science of genetics has revealed the complex structure of the cell and how traits are passed on from generation to generation. Paleontology has shown that living things have never changed.

Darwinism finds itself. So great is the logical collapse Darwinists exhibited that they never even consider the question of "How were the flies the reptiles were chasing able to fly?"

The fact is that flies have an utterly immaculate flight system.

While human beings cannot flap their arms even 10 times a second, an average fly is able to beat its wings 500 times a second. In addition, both its wings beat simultaneously. The slightest discrepancy between the movements of the two wings would cause the fly to lose balance. If the Darwinists' claims were true, then a great many other animals famed for their high speed also would chase flies, and lions,

The countless mosquito fossils discovered to date show that these animals have always been mosquitoes, that they did not evolve from any other life form, and that they never underwent any intermediate stages.

One of the main features of the fossil record is that living things remain unchanged over the course of very lengthy periods of geological time. There is no difference between this 50-millionyear- old fossil fly and specimens alive today.

Boar Skull
Period: Paleocene
Age: 58 million years
Location: China

Darwinists were able to gather their original supporters by using a very primitive logic. In a climate of scientific ignorance, it was easy to convince the public that proteins and eventually, cells could form spontaneously from muddy water that mammals hunting in water eventually developed fins and turned into dolphins and thatmonkeys decided to stop leaping from tree to tree and instead to walk upright, and thus evolved into human beings.

The sciences of genetics and paleontology were unknown, so all these imaginary transitions were depicted as incontrovertible fact. But now Darwinists are in a far more difficult position. The science of genetics has revealed the complex structure of the cell and how traits are passed on from generation to generation. Paleontology has shown that living things have never changed.

## The Darwinist deception on the subject of birds and the origin of flight

According to one of the evolution scenario's claims, some water-dwelling amphibians developed into fully terrestrial reptiles. One branch of this group evolved further, constituting the ancestors of today's birds.

According to evolutionist claims, these imaginary creatures descended from their alleged reptilian ancestors some 150 to 200 million years ago, acquiring new characteristics gradually and in stages until they emerged as fully-fledged birds. As this scenario requires, their attempts at flight also emerged in stages before taking on its presently flawless ability.

However, despite all the efforts expended over the last century and a half, not a single trace has ever been found of the half-bird, half-reptile creatures that evolutionists assume must once have lived. No transitional forms covered half in scales and half in feathers, or with halfdeveloped wings, have ever been found in the Earth's geological strata. In fact, contrary to what's been conjectured, only fossils with

**(1) A fully formed dinosaur, many examples of which are seen in the fossil record.**

DINO-BIRDS ARE SOLELY THE PRODUCTS OF THE IMAGINATION

**(2)**

**(3)**

perfect structures—the remains of flawless, fully formed living things—have ever been discovered.

One of evolutionists' most unbelievable claims is the thesis they propose to account for how terrestrial animals supposedly began to fly. According to this tale, one that even primary school children would find ridiculous, the forearms of reptiles that hunted flies eventually turned into wings, and the animals began flying. This thesis, a complete misery of logic, is just one of the countless examples of the desperate straits in which

In order to be able to prove that birds evolved from dinosaurs, evolutionists would have had to have discovered the supposed transitional form fossils shown in the illustrations to the side. However, although many fossils of both birds and dinosaurs have been unearthed, the fossil record contains no trace of supposed dino-birds. Defective life forms with missing organs, bearing half-bird and half-reptile characteristics, which should have existed in large numbers according to evolutionist claims, appear nowhere in any of the Earth's strata.

The life forms in the fossil record are all flawless and complete. None are semi-developed of the kind seen in these pictures. This fact is important evidence that evolution never happened.

**FICTITIOUS DRAWINGS**

(5)

(5) A complete bird of which we see thousands of specimens.

(4)

(2, 3, 4) There exists not the slightest jotof evidence that such semi-formed living things ever existed.

The evolutionists' "transitional form predicament" also applies to the origin of birds. According to evolutionist claims, "single winged" and "half winged" entities should have existed; but had they existed, the fossil record should corroborate that. However, the subjects of these evolutionist scenarios are no more than reports and fictitious drawings based on no scientific evidence whatsoever. Life forms have always appeared suddenly at all periods of history, and have always had complete and fully functioning organs.

Darwinism finds itself. So great is the logical collapse Darwinists exhibited that they never even consider the question of "How were the flies the reptiles were chasing able to fly?"

The fact is that flies have an utterly immaculate flight system.

While human beings cannot flap their arms even 10 times a second, an average fly is able to beat its wings 500 times a second. In addition, both its wings beat simultaneously. The slightest discrepancy between the movements of the two wings would cause the fly to lose balance. If the Darwinists' claims were true, then a great many other animals famed for their high speed also would chase flies, and lions,

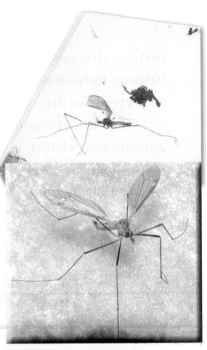

The countless mosquito fossils discovered to date show that these animals have always been mosquitoes, that they did not evolve from any other life form, and that they never underwent any intermediate stages.

One of the main features of the fossil record is that living things remain unchanged over the course of very lengthy periods of geological time. There is no difference between this 50-millionyear- old fossil fly and specimens alive today.

leopards, cheetahs and horses should also one day have grown wings and started flying. Darwinists adorn these claims with scientific and Latin terminology, and millions of people naively believe them. The fact is, though, scientific findings openly and clearly reveal the invalidity of evolutionist claims. Not a single example of a living thing gradually acquiring wings has ever been encountered in the fossil record. Research reveals that any such transition is impossible.

Specimens of winged insects are frequently encountered in the fossil record, some of which are 300 million years old. The fossil march fly in the picture is 50 million years old.

ACCORDING TO THE EVOLUTIONIST DREAM—OR RATHER, NIGHTMARE—, THIS SHOULD BE THE CASE

Believing in Darwinist claims regarding the origin of flight means believing that cheetahs will someday gain wings and fly, and that tigers will one day turn into giant birds. No rational person could ever accept such an irrational claim.

Confuciusornis
Period: Cretaceous
Age: 120 million years
Location: China

The theory of evolution claims that birds evolved from small therapod dinosaurs—in other words, from reptiles. The fact is, however, that anatomical comparisons between birds and reptiles refute this claim, as does the fossil record.

The fossil pictured belongs to an extinct species of bird known as Confuciusornis, the first specimenof which was discovered in China in 1995. Confuciusornis bears a very close resemblance to present-day birds and has demolished the scenario of bird evolution that evolution-

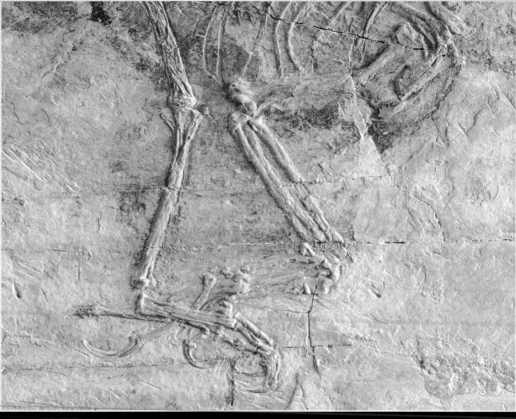

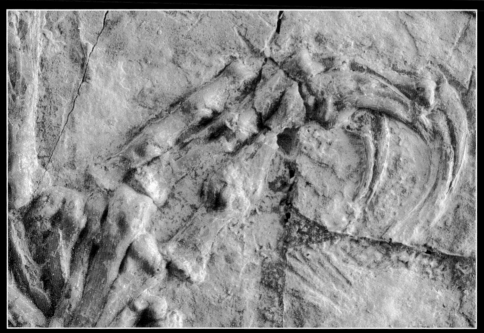

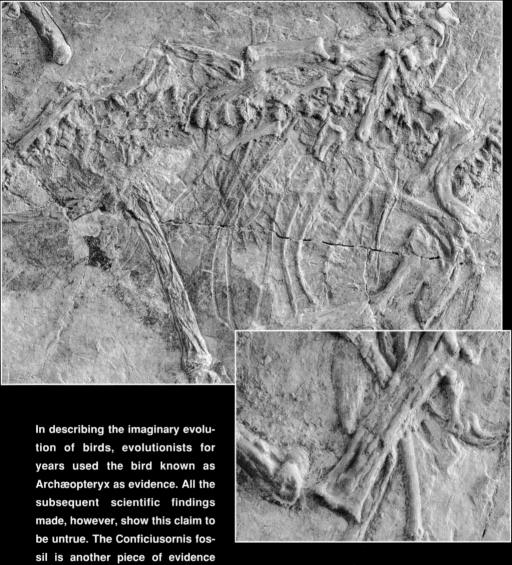

In describing the imaginary evolution of birds, evolutionists for years used the bird known as Archæopteryx as evidence. All the subsequent scientific findings made, however, show this claim to be untrue. The Conficiusornis fossil is another piece of evidence showing that Archæopteryx cannot be the supposed forerunner of birds. This bird, from the same period as Archæopteryx (around 140 million years ago), has no teeth. Its beak and feathers have the same characteristics as those of present-day birds. Its skeletal structure is also identical to that of modern-day birds, and it has talons on its wings, as does Archæopteryx. The structure known as the pygostyle, which supports the tail feathers, is also present in this bird. In short, this creature, the same age as Archæopteryx—which evolutionists regard as the oldest supposed forebear of birds, as being half-reptile and half-bird—bears a very close resemblance to modern-day birds. This fact refutes evolutionist theses to the effect that Archæopteryx is the primitive forerunner of all birds.

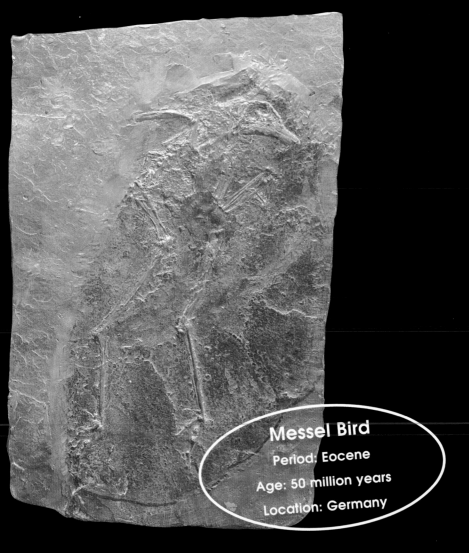

**Messel Bird**

Period: Eocene

Age: 50 million years

Location: Germany

The bird fossil was named for having been discovered in the famous Messel shales. None of the bodily mechanisms of birds, which have a completely different structure from terrestrial life forms, can be explained in terms of any gradual evolutionary model. First of all, wings—the most important feature that makes birds what they are—represent a complete impasse for the theory of evolution. Evolutionists themselves state the impossibility of a reptile being able to fly and indeed, that this claim is contradicted by the fossil record. The ornithologist Alan Feduccia, for example, asks, "How do you derive birds from a heavy, earthbound, bipedal reptile that has a deep body, a heavy balancing tail, and fore-shortened forelimbs? Biophysically, it's impossible." ("Jurassic Bird Challenges Origin Theories," Geotimes, January 1996, p. 7.)

Yet another discovery that invalidates evolutionist claims regarding the origin of birds is the Liaoningornis fossil shown here. The existence of this bird, around 140 million years of age and first discovered in China in November 1996, was announced by the ornithologists Lianhin Hou, and Martin and Alan Feduccia in an article published in Science magazine.

Liaoningornis had a breastbone to which the flight muscles were attached, as in present-day birds.

It was also identical to birds living today in all other respects. The sole difference was that it had teeth in its jaw. This showed that odontornithes (toothed birds) by no means had the kind of primitive structure claimed by evolutionists. Indeed, in an analysis in Discover magazine Alan Feduccia stated that Liaoningornis invalidated the claim that dinosaurs constitute the origin of birds. ("Old Bird," Discover, 21 March 1997.)

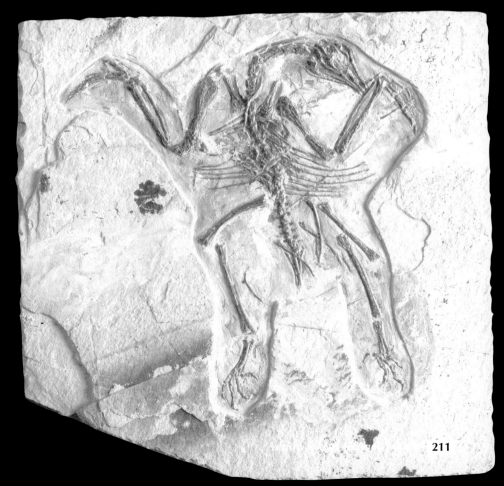

**Liaoxiornis**

Period: Cretaceous

Age: 144-65 million years

Location: China

All the fossils unearthed show that birds have always existed as birds, and that they have not evolved from any other life form. Darwinists, who maintain that birds evolved from terrestrial animals, are actually well aware of this, and are unable to account for how wings and the flight mechanism emerged through an evolutionary process and through random mechanisms such as mutation. The Turkish biologist Engin Korur admits the impossibility of wing evolution: "The common feature of eyes and wings is that they can perform their functions only when they are fully developed. To put it another way, sight is impossible with a deficient eye, and flight is impossible with half a wing. How these organs appeared is still one of those secrets of nature that have not yet been fully illuminated." (Engin Korur, "Gozlerin ve Kanatlarin Sirri" ("The Secret of Eyes and Wings"), Bilim ve Teknik, No. 203, October 1984, p. 25.)

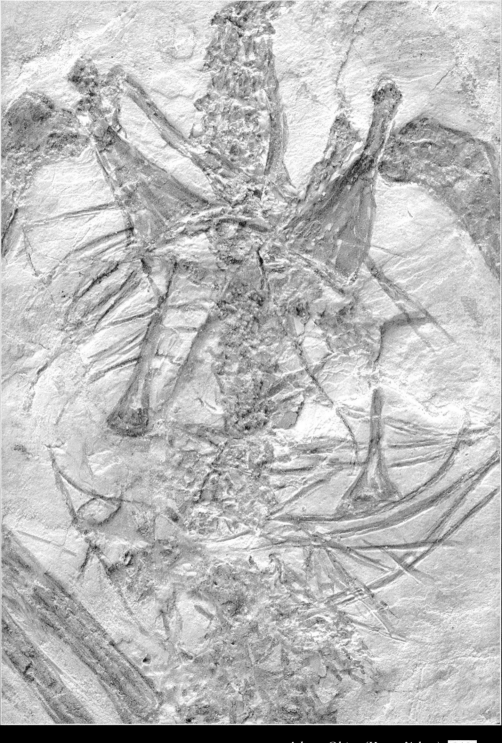

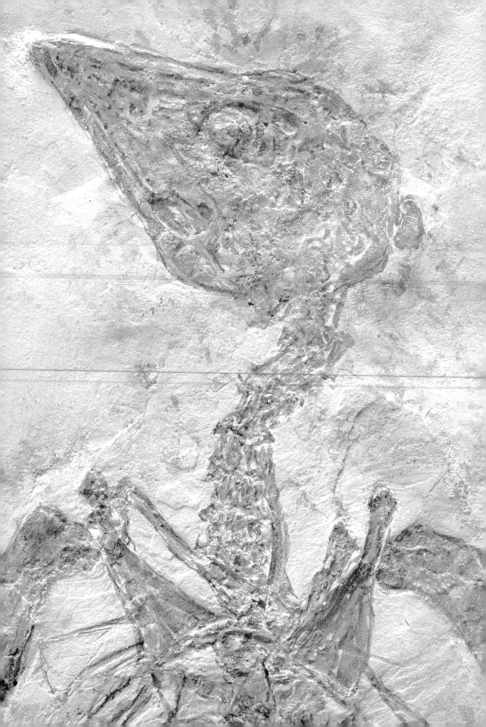

Powerful wing muscles must be securely attached to the bird's breastbone, and have a structure suitable for lifting the bird into the air and establishing balance and movement in all directions when aloft. It is also essential that bird's wing and tail feathers be light, flexible and in proportion to one another—that they should have a perfect aerodynamic framework making flight possible.

At this point, the theory of evolution faces a major dilemma: The question of how this wing's

flawless structure could have emerged as the result of a succession of random mutations goes unanswered. "Evolution" can never explain how a reptile's forelegs could have developed into a flawless wing as the result of impairments in its genes—that is, mutations.

As the quotation cited on the preceding page states, flight is impossible with just a half wing. Therefore, even if we assume that a mutation of some kind did cause some kind of changes in a reptile's forelegs, it is still irrational to expect that a wing could emerge by chance, as a result of other mutations being added on. Any mutation in the front legs would not endow the animal with wings, but would deprive it of the use of its forelegs. This would leave the creature physically disadvantaged (crippled, in other words) compared to other members of its species.

According to biophysical research, mutations take place only very rarely. Therefore, it is impossible to expect such handicapped creatures to wait for millions of years for their half-formed, functionless wings to be completed by small mutations.

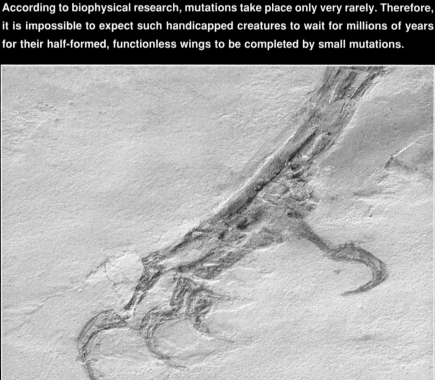

Confuciusornis Sanctus
Period: Cretaceous
Age: 120 million years
Location: China

The French scientific journal Science et Vie made the following comment regarding this bird, now known as Confuciusornis sanctus:

"According to Chinese and American palaeontologists examining the fossil . . . they were dealing with a first class discovery. This flying bird, the same approximate size as a water rail, is around 157 million years old . . . older than Archœopteryx." (Jean Philippe Noel, "Les Oiseaux de la Discorde," Science et Vie, No. 961, October 1997, p. 83.)

The significance of this discovery is obvious; the fact that Confuciusornis lived during the same period as a life form claimed to have been the supposed forerunner of birds—and the fact that it bears a very close similarity to present-day birds—totally invalidates evolutionists' claims.

There are several structural differences between birds and reptiles, one of the most important of these being bone structure. The bones of dinosaurs—regarded by evolutionists as the supposed ancestors of birds—are thick and solid, making them very heavy. On the other hand, the bones of birds—both living and extinct species—are all hollow and thus very light, which is of great importance in their being able to fly.

Another difference between birds and reptiles is their different metabolic rates. Reptiles have one of the slowest metabolisms of all life forms on Earth, while birds hold the highest. Due to a sparrow's very fast metabolism, for example, its body temperature may sometimes rise to as high as 48°C (118.4 F). Reptiles are unable to generate their own body heat, warming their bodies by basking in the sun's rays. Reptiles consume energy the slowest, while birds consume it the highest of all.

Despite his being an evolutionist, Alan Feduccia strongly opposes the theory that birds and dinosaurs are related, on the basis of scientific findings. On the subject of the dino-bird evolution thesis, he has this to say:

Well, I've studied bird skulls for 25 years and I don't see any similarities whatsoever. I just don't see it . . . The theropod origins of birds, in my opinion, will be the greatest embarrassment of paleontology of the 20th century. (Pat Shipman, "Birds Do It ... Did Dinosaurs?," New Scientist, 1 February 1997, p. 28.)

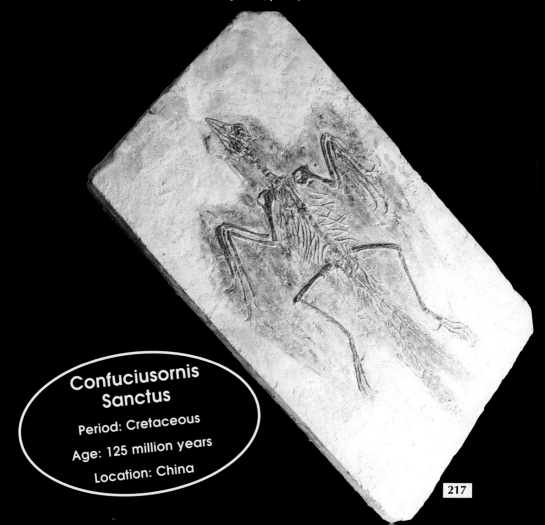

Confuciusornis
Sanctus

Period: Cretaceous

Age: 125 million years

Location: China

217

# Fossil Specimens of Insects

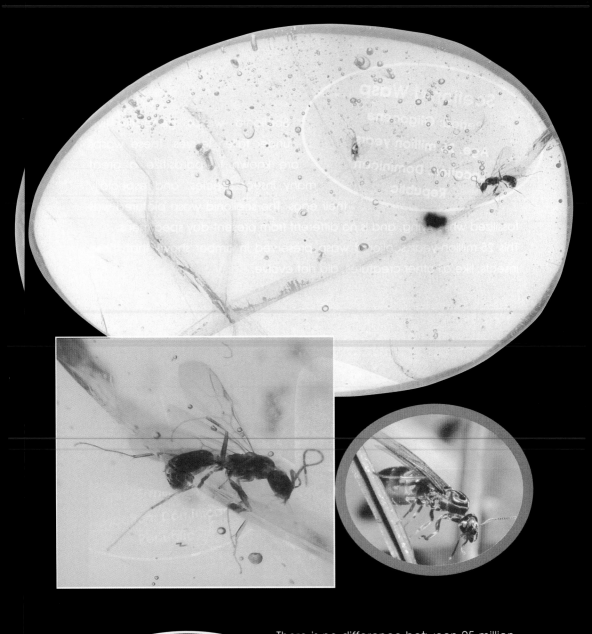

### Worker Ant

Period: Oligocene

Age: 25 million years

Location: Dominican Republic

There is no difference between 25-million-year-old winged ants and specimens alive today. Winged ants that have remained the same despite the passage of millions of years are some of the proofs that evolution never happened.

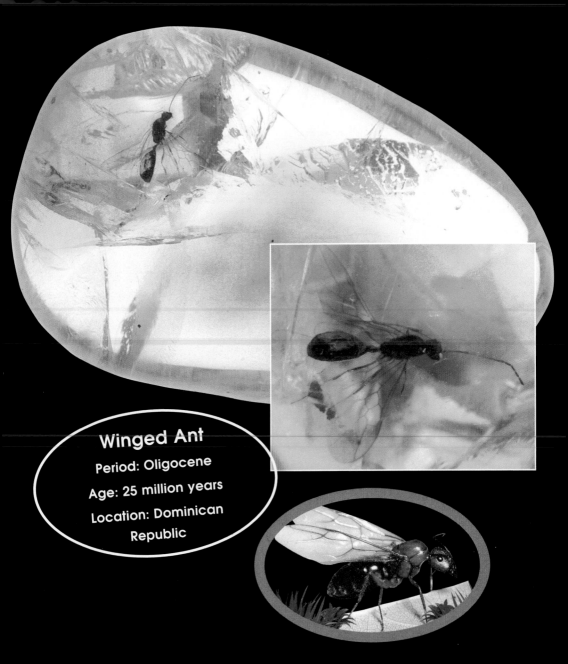

## Winged Ant

**Period:** Oligocene

**Age:** 25 million years

**Location:** Dominican Republic

Winged ants have two long wings 5 to 8 millimeters (1.9 to 3.1 in) in length. They build their nests close to sources of food and water. These ants have remained unchanged for millions of years. The fossil ant in 25-million-year-old amber shows that these insects have been remained the same for millions of years, in other words, they did not undergo evolution.

## Scelionid Wasp

**Period:** Oligocene
**Age:** 25 million years
**Location:** Dominican Republic

Scelionid wasps generally live under fallen leaves. These wasps are known to parasitize a great many insect species, and especially their eggs. The scelionid wasp pictured was fossilized while flying, and is no different from present-day spec mens.

This 25-million-year scelionid wasp preserved in amber shows that these insects, like all other creatures, did not evolve.

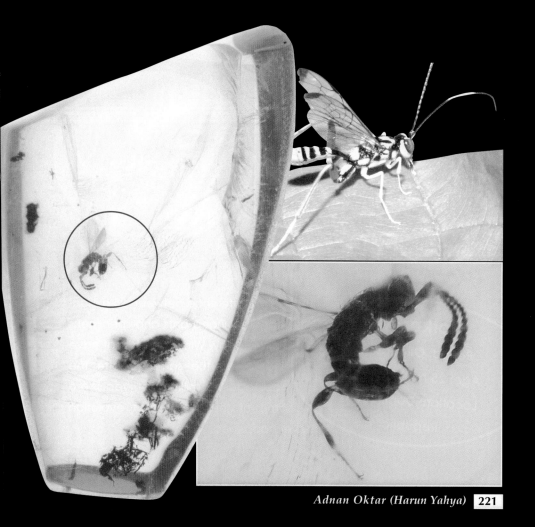

*Adnan Oktar (Harun Yahya)* **221**

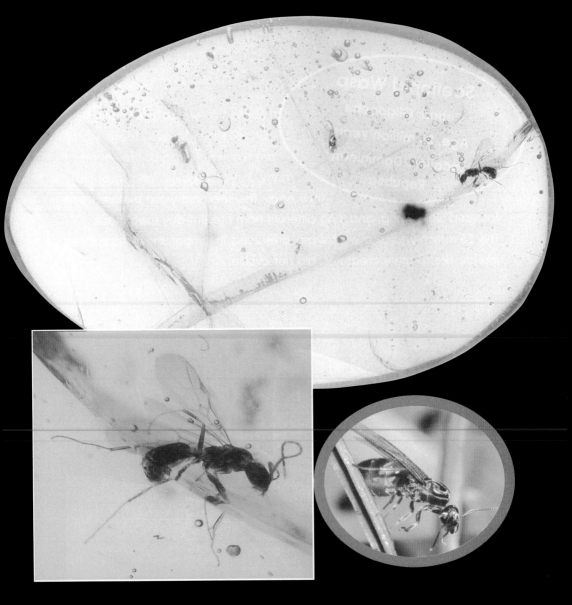

## Worker Ant

**Period:** Oligocene

**Age:** 25 million years

**Location:** Dominican Republic

There is no difference between 25-million-year-old winged ants and specimens alive today. Winged ants that have remained the same despite the passage of millions of years are some of the proofs that evolution never happened.

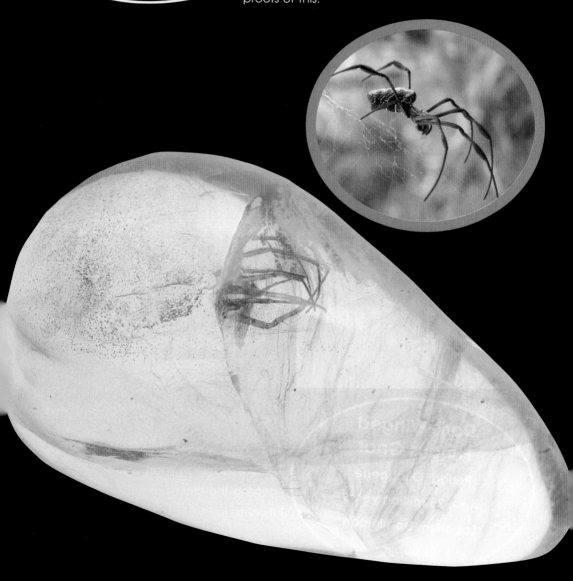

## Spider

**Period:** Oligocene

**Age:** 25 million years

**Location:** Dominican Republic

Spiders today possess all the features possessed by those that lived millions of years ago. A 25-million-year- old spider fossilized in amber is one of the proofs of this.

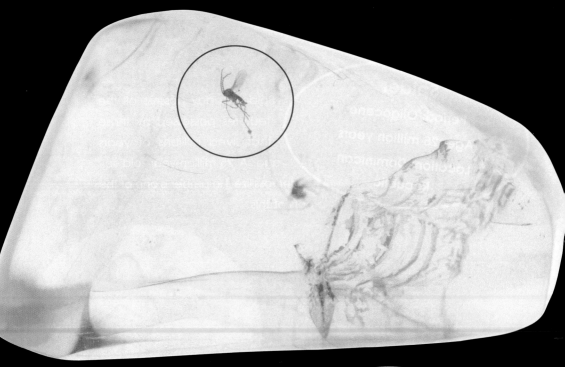

## Dark-Winged Fungus Gnat

**Period: Oligocene**

**Age: 25 million years**

**Location: Dominican Republic**

This dark-winged fungus gnat is 25 million years old, defying the claims of evolutionists.

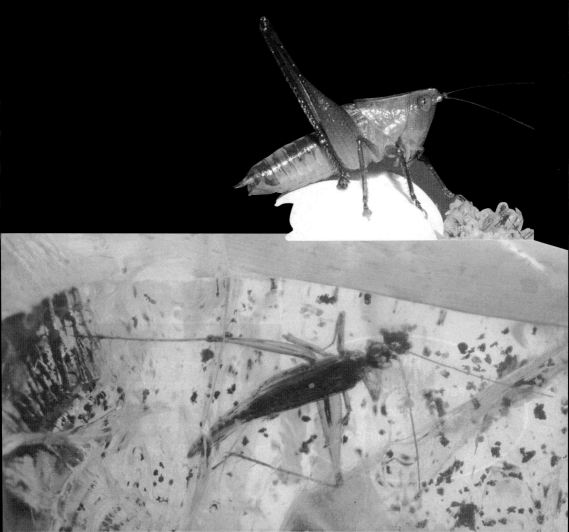

**Grasshopper**
Period: Oligocene
Age: 25 million years
Location: Dominican Republic

Specimens of fossilized grasshoppers are identical to those living today. The fact that grasshoppers that lived 25 million years ago were identical to present-day specimens shows that evolution never happened.

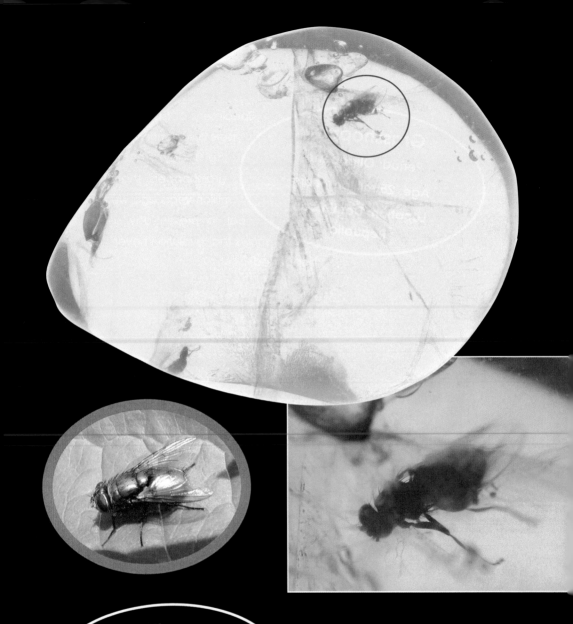

## Fly

**Period:** Oligocene

**Age:** 25 million years

**Location:** Dominican Republic

Flies have always existed as flies, and are not descended from any other life form and have undergone no intermediate stages. One of the proofs of this is this fossil in 25-million-year-old amber in the picture.

There is no difference between springtails that lived 25 million years ago and those alive today.

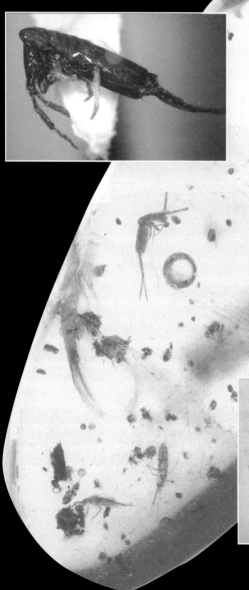

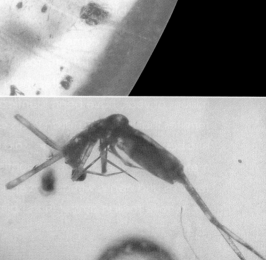

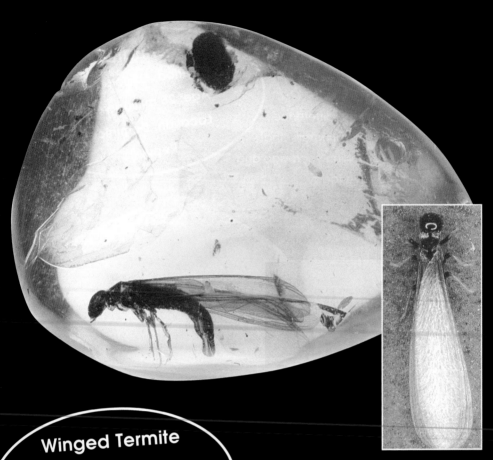

## Winged Termite

**Period:** Oligocene
**Age:** 25 million years
**Location:** Dominican Republic

Although termites resemble ants, they actually possess very different characteristics and abilities. Termites have been living in colonies for millions of years and have come down to the present day with their structures totally unchanged. Termite fossils 250 million years old are one of the proofs of this. All the termites that have ever lived during the intervening millions of years have been identical to those living today. Just like worker termites that lived 250 million years ago, those living today engage in altruistic behavior, feed the larvae, soldiers and queens, and build nests many meters in size—despite being sightless. The characteristics of present-day termites also apply, without exception, to all termites that have ever lived. The termite fossil in amber in the picture is 25 million years old.

There are millions of fossils that literally silence Darwinism. One of the fossils that leave Darwinists utterly helpless is this earwig in 25-million-year-old amber. As with all other fossil findings, this fossil shows that evolution is invalid.

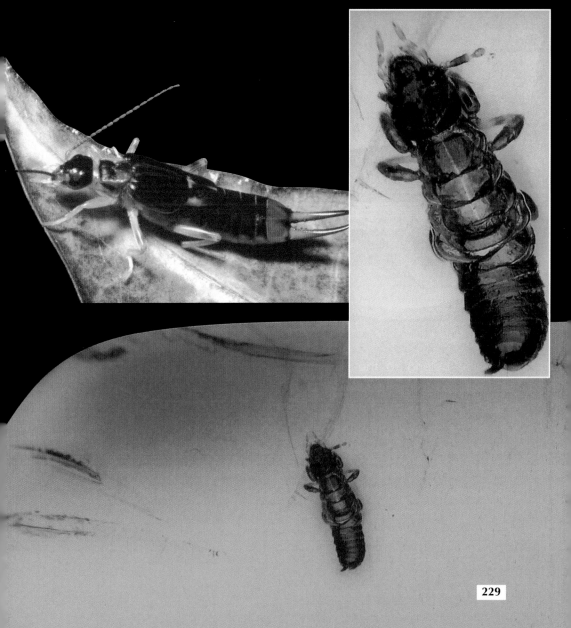

**Earwig**
Period: Oligocene
Age: 25 million years
Location: Dominican Republic

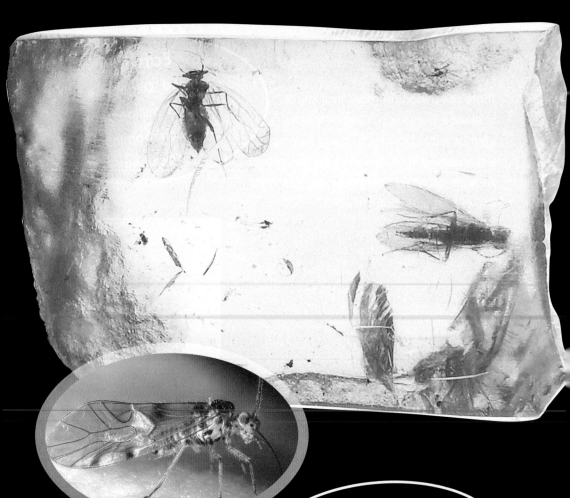

**Barklouse**

Period: Cretaceous

Age: 100 million years

Location: Myanmar

Barklice belong to the order Psocoptera. The earliest known fossils date back to the Permian Period (290 to 248 million years ago). The bark louse pictured lived 100 million years earlier, in the Cretaceous Period (144 to 65 million years ago). With their wings, eyes and other organs, barklice have remained unchanged for hundreds of millions of years and invalidate scenarios stemming from evolutionists' imaginations.

Insect species belonging to the order Hemiptera include bedbugs, true bugs and other hemipterous insects. The assassin bug pictured is another member of this order. When examined, these modern-day insects can be seen to be identical to this 25-million-year-old fossil.

This completely invalidates the myth of insect evolution. Insects never evolved, as Darwinists maintain. Our Almighty Lord has created all living things in the form of different species. Insects are one of these different forms and, as can be seen in this specimen, have remained unchanged for millions of years.

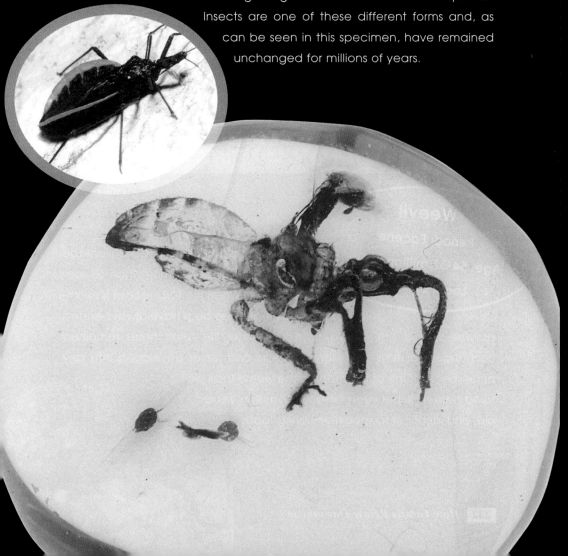

**Assassin Bug**
Period: Oligocene
Age: 25 million years
Location: Dominican Republic

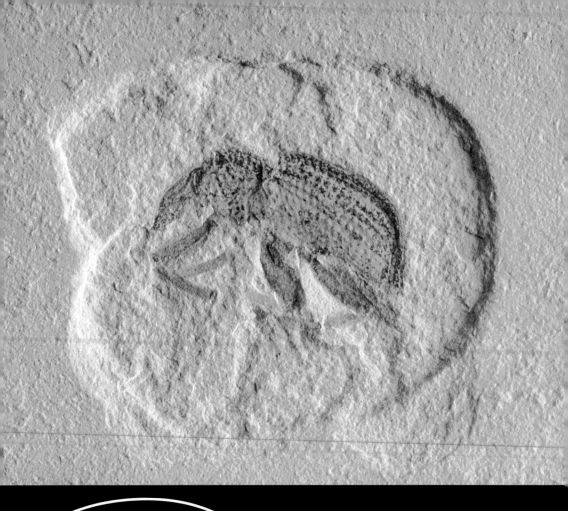

## Weevil

**Period: Eocene**
**Age: 54-37 million years**
**Location: USA**

Weevils, part of the Curculionidae superfamily, represent more than 60 separate species. When the fossil record is examined, it appears that these bugs have always existed as weevils, did not evolve from any other life form, have remained unchanged for tens of millions of years and never developed into any other species. One of the proofs is the weevil fossil pictured here. It is between 54 and 37 million years old, and identical to specimens living today.

With its structure and appearance, which have not altered for tens of millions of years, the marchfly is one of the countless life forms that challenge the theory of evolution.

These insects, which average 3 to 12 millimeters (0.1 to 0.4 in) in length, emerge in the springtime, live close to the surface of the soil, and damage plants. The organisms belonging to this family are some of the oldest known flies.

**Marchfly**

Period: Eocene

Age: 50 million years

Location: Canada

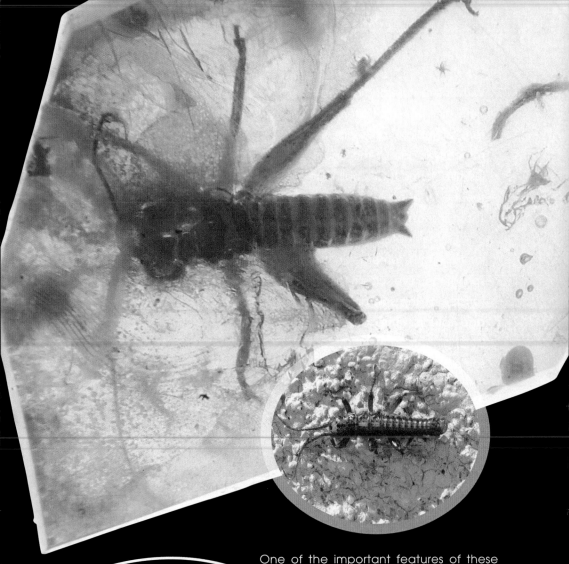

## Walking Stick

PPeriod: Eocene

Age: 50 million years

Location: Poland

One of the important features of these creatures, members of the family Phasmatidae, is their ability to change color, depending on light, temperature, humidity and even the abundance of food. This change comes about through an alteration in the density and location of pigment, or else through the formation of new pigment.* The 50-million-year-old fossil walking stick pictured was also able to change colors, just like specimens living today.

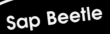

## Sap Beetle

**Period:** Oligocene
**Age:** 25 million years
**Location:** Dominican Republic

Of those insects belonging to the family Nitidulidae (Coleoptera), only those living on flowers are regarded as pests. The great majority of species feed on pollen and sap. Coleoptera alive today have exactly the same characteristics as those that lived millions of years ago. This fact, confirmed by fossil discoveries, is an indication that the insects in question did not form in stages, in other words that they did not evolve.

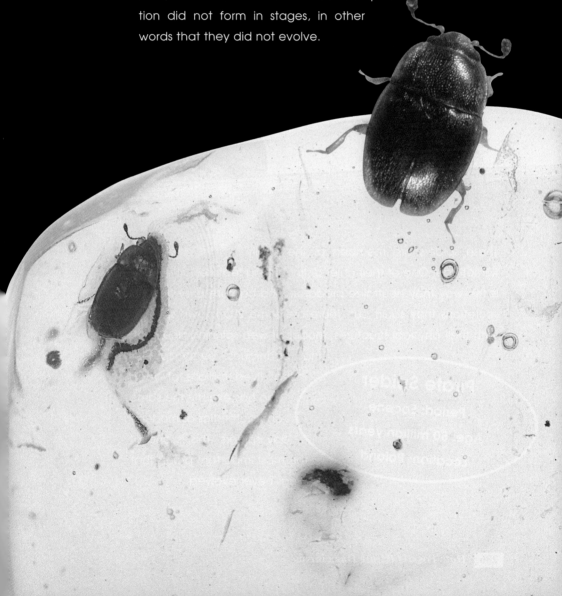

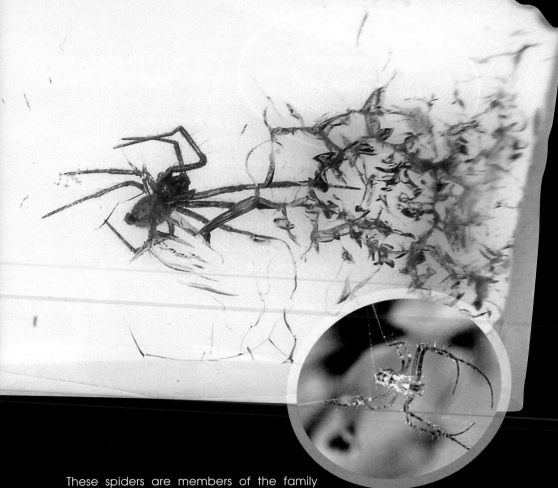

These spiders are members of the family
Mimetidae. One of their chief distinguishing features
is the way they neutralize predators and capture prey through
secretions they squirt out. There are some 200 known species.
With their physical structures, modes of web-spinning and hunting techniques, every species
that lived millions of years
ago has exactly the same
characteristics as modern-
day spiders. This is one of
the most important proofs that
living things never evolved.

**Pirate Spider**

Period: Eocene

Age: 50 million years

Location: Poland

Like this long-legged fly pictured, the hundreds of fossils in this book (and the billions on Earth) are clear proofs that no such thing as evolution ever took place, and that living things emerged on Earth perfectly formed and in a single moment. In other words, they were created. Almighty God, Lord of the Earth and sky and all that lies between, created the entire universe and all the infinite number of entities, living and non-living, within it. Led astray by a preconception, evolutionists defend this theory in terrible ignorance.

One of the best responses to them is given by fossils, which clearly and indisputable reveal that evolution is a myth.

Age: 45 million years
Location: Russia

One of the most important abilities of dragonflies is their enormous maneuverability. No matter at what speed or which direction it may be flying, the dragonfly can suddenly stop and head off again in the opposite direction. Alternatively, it can hover in the air and wait for a suitable position from which to attack its prey. From that position it can make a sharp turn and approach the prey.

In a very short space of time, it can attain 40 kilometers/hour (25 mph), an astonishing speed for an insect. (Olympic 100-meter sprinters manage only 39 kilometers/hour (24.2 mph).) It is impossible to account for the magnificent way in which the dragonfly uses its wings by any model of

**Drangonfly and Mayfly Larva**
Period: Cretaceous
Age: 128 million years
Location: China

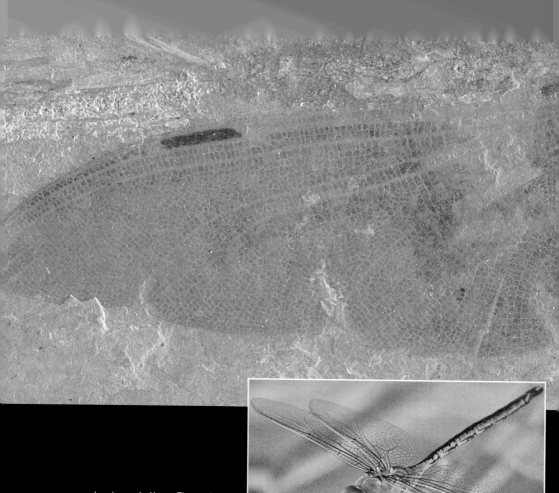

gradual evolution. The wing represents a complete impasse for evolutionists. There is no difference between the oldest dragonfly fossils yet discovered and specimens alive today. There is no trace of any "semi-dragonfly" or a dragonfly whose wings were just developing that lived before the earliest known dragonfly. Like other living things, these insects emerged suddenly and have survived unchanged down to the present day. In other words, they were created by God and never evolved at all.

## Stick Insect

**Period: Eocene**

**Age: 45 million years**

**Location: Russia**

The stick insects are known for their ponderously slow movements and superb camouflage. With their long bodies, antennae and colors, they do indeed resemble slender twigs. It can sometimes be difficult to tell a stick insect on a plant apart from the plant itself.

Animals that use various forms of camouflage enjoy special protection with their bodily structures, shapes, colors and patterns, all created to match the environments they inhabit. As can be seen in this specimen, living things possess wellorganized, complex structures that totally invalidate the theory of evolution's claims of "chance." Every living thing bears its own evidence that it was created. The ability to employ camouflage is just one of these pieces of evidence.

A. Brouwer, author of the book General Paleontology, summarizes the defeat suffered by Darwinism at the hands of fossils:

"One of the most surprising negative results of paleontological research in the last century is that such transitional forms seem to be inordinately scarce. In Darwin's time this could perhaps be ascribed with some justification to the incompleteness of the paleontological record and to lack of knowledge, but with the enormous number of fossil species which have been discovered since then, other causes must be found for the almost complete absence of transitional forms." (A. Brouwer, General Paleontology (translated by R. H. Kaye), Edinburgh & London: Oliver & Boyd, 1967, pp. 162-163)

Evolutionists do not need to "look for excuses," as Brouwer puts it, but to see the facts. Countless fossils, such as the 125-million-year-old wasp fossil pictured here, show that evolution never took place, and that living things are created.

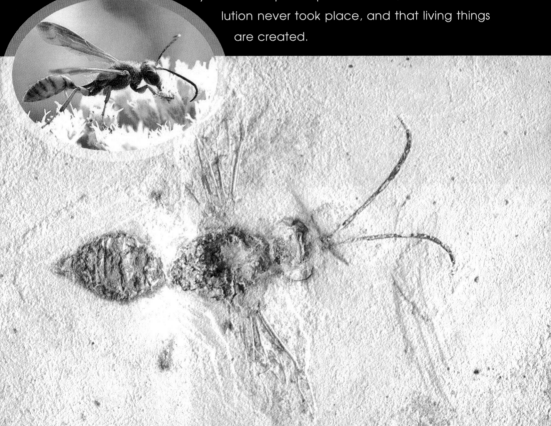

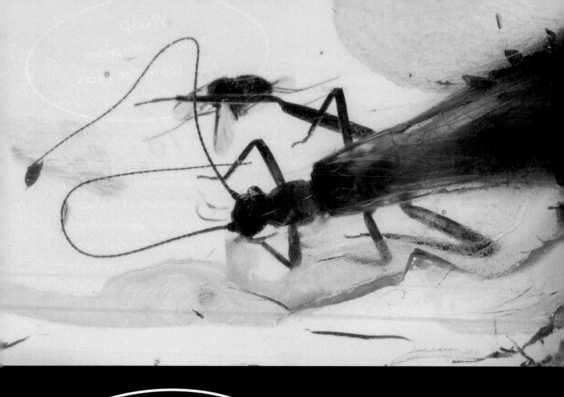

## Stone Fly

**Period: Eocene**

**Age: 50 million years**

**Location: Russia**

Stone flies range between 5 and 10 millimeters (0.1 and 0.3 in) in length and have twolong antennae; their larvae are used as fishing bait. They too have remained unchanged for millions of years. This 50-million-year-old fossil stone fly pictured is identical to stone flies living today.

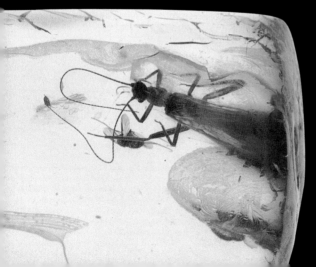

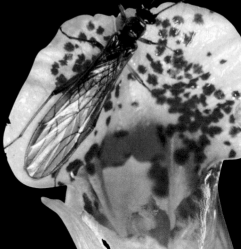

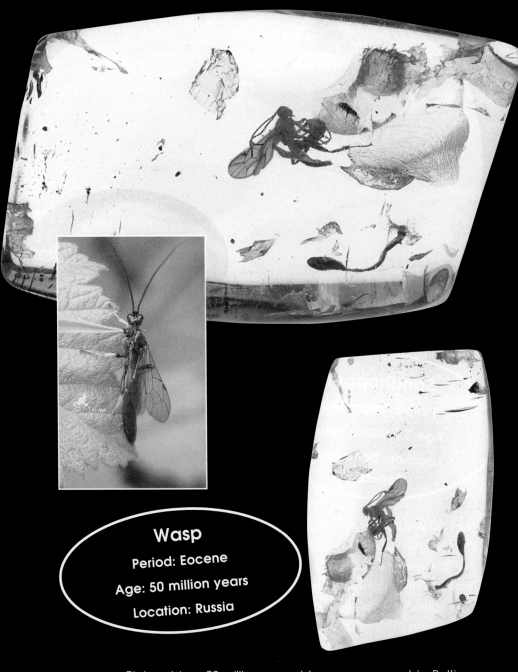

## Wasp

**Period: Eocene**

**Age: 50 million years**

**Location: Russia**

Pictured is a 50-million-year-old wasp preserved in Baltic amber. Like all other living things, wasps, which have remained the same for 50 million years, show that evolution never happened, and that God created them.

## Sandhopper

Period: Oligocene

Age: 25 million years

Location: Dominican Republic

Amphipods, reminiscent of wood lice in terms of their general appearance, are represented by two sub-orders. They mainly live in deep seas and fresh water, while some species also live in warm, humid locations on dry land. One of the most important features of those living by the shore is their very powerful sense of direction.

It is God Who creates, knows and Who at every moment keeps under control the universe, the galaxies with their extraordinary balances, life on Earth, all the known and unknown varieties of living things, their life styles, and human beings—as well as a single enzyme in the DNA possessed by every living thing, a single leaf that falls from just one of all the billions of trees in the world, a single micro-organism on the surface of that leaf, and the organelles in that micro-organism responsible for photosynthesis.

It is certainly an easy for Almighty God to create countless living things, all very different to one another at the time He chooses, and all in a single moment. The 25-million-year-old sandhopper pictured is one of the proofs of God's sublime creation.

With their superior flight techniques and eye structure, gall midges represent a major dilemma for evolutionists.

It is impossible to account for such complex structures as wings and eyes in terms of gradual formation. No fossil fly with only partly developed wings has so far been encountered. All fossil flies are complete, with fully formed wings, visual systems and other structures. These findings condemn evolutionists to a profound silence, because they mean that living things did not evolve, but were created by God.

**Gall Midge**
Period: Cretaceous
Age: 100 million years
Location: Myanmar

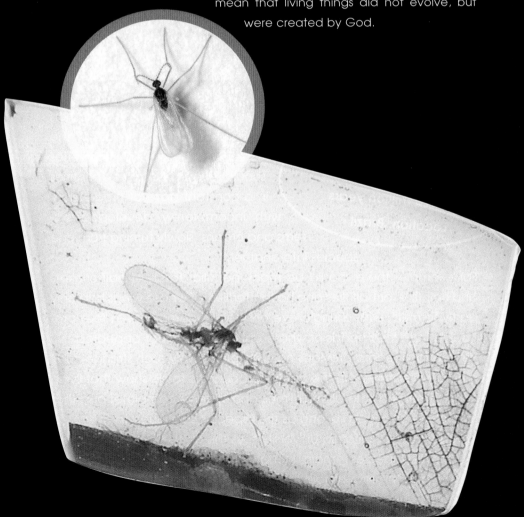

**Mayfly**

Period: Cretaceous

Age: 125 million years

Location: Brazil

If, as claimed, all living things evolved, then signs of this should be visible in the fossil record. Fossil discoveries should reveal the traces of entities in a constant state of progression, with incompletely developed systems and organs, slowly turning from one species into another.

For example, there should be many peculiar fossils of half-crickets and half-flies, or half flies and halfbutterflies, or whose wings had only partly formed, with a single eye on their abdomens, with feet protruding from their heads or whose antennae had not appeared.

Yet the fossil record provides no examples of any such strange, rudimentary creatures. On the contrary, countless fossils show that living things emerged with all their limbs and systems complete, and that they never changed so long as their species continued to exist. D. S. Woodroff from California University says this on the subject:

"But fossil species remain unchanged throughout most of their history and the record fails to contain a single example of a significant transition." (D. S. Woodroff, Science, vol. 208, 1980, p. 716)

There are some 1,000,000 known insect species living on Earth, and some 15,000 fossil species. Every year, several thousand more species of insect are discovered. Each of them has entirely different systems, metabolisms and habitats.

Evolutionists maintain that all these species gradually developed from one another by way of very small changes. However, they cannot pinpoint the fist supposed ancestor of insects, nor any imaginary family relationship between species. They desperately look for fossils that could indicate these. Yet every new fossil acquired reveals that this insect species came into being out of nothing, with all its particular characteristics. In other words, it was created, and that has remained unchanged for tens or even hundreds of millions of years—meaning that it never underwent evolution.

One of the proofs of this state of affairs is the 125-million-year-old fossilized planthopper pictured here. Identical in every way to planthoppers alive today, this fossil refutes evolution.

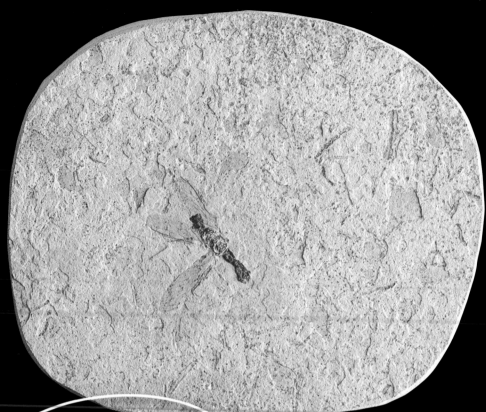

## Snake Fly

**Period: Cretaceous**

**Age: 125 million years**

**Location: Brazil**

Snake flies, of which there are estimated to be 150 or so species, are members of the class Raphidioptera—another life form showing that evolution never took place. In fact, scientific circles are well aware that the fossil record does not support evolution. But because of their ideological dependance on the theory, they never openly admit this fact.

Dragonflies are known to have been in existence for some 300 million years. And with their extraordinary wing structures and flying systems, they inflict a heavy blow on Darwinism. Three hundred million years ago, at a time when it is claimed that only primitive life forms and a primitive environment supposedly existed, dragonflies already possessed a flawless flying system that's now used as a model for the most advanced helicopters. And those insects' system has undergone not the slightest change right down to the present. Dragonfly larvae have also had exactly the same anatomy for hundreds of millions of years, and have used the exact same structural mechanisms to catch prey. It is impossible to account for this state of affairs in evolutionary terms.

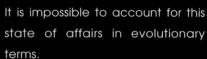

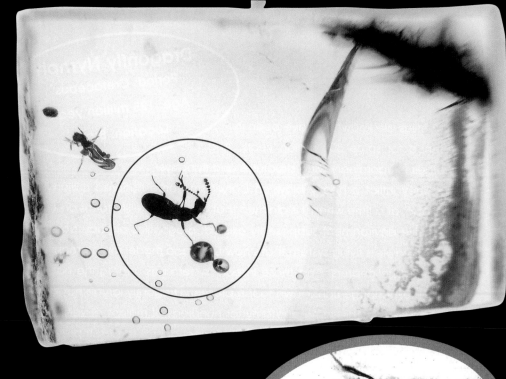

**Ant-Like Stone Beetle**

Period: Cretaceous

Age: 100 million years

Location: Myanmar

One hundred million years is a relatively long time for any life form's completion of the supposed evolutionary development. If evolutionists' views were accurate, then over the course of all that time, ant-like stone beetles should have turned into very different forms and should bear no resemblance to beetles still alive today. Yet despite the passage of millions of years, ant-like stone beetles—like all other life forms—have undergone not the slightest change. They were the same 100 million years ago as they are today, which makes any reference to evolution impossible.

**Mayfly Nymph**

Period: Cretaceous

Age: 125 million years

Location: Brazil

Larvae such as those of the mayfly have remained just the same for as long as they have been in existence. The 125-million-year-old mayfly nymph pictured here is proof of this.

Both mayflies and their larvae, stages of insects that have remained unchanged over tens of millions of years, silence evolutionists.

# Deathwatch Beetle

**Period: Eocene**

**Age: 45 million years**

**Location: Russia**

Like all other beetles, this deathwatch beetle preserved in amber that dates back to the Eocene epoch (54 to 37 million years ago) possesses very interesting characteristics. During their larval stage, deathwatch beetles store the nutrients they need as fat tissue and use them during their adult stage, not taking on any further nutrients from the outside. These insects, which live in wood, are able to digest cellulose with the help of bacteria and fungi in their stomachs.

During the mating period, they knock on the tunnels they've dug in the wood, producing a noise that can easily be heard by human beings. Deathwatch beetles have had these fascinating characteristics for millions of years.

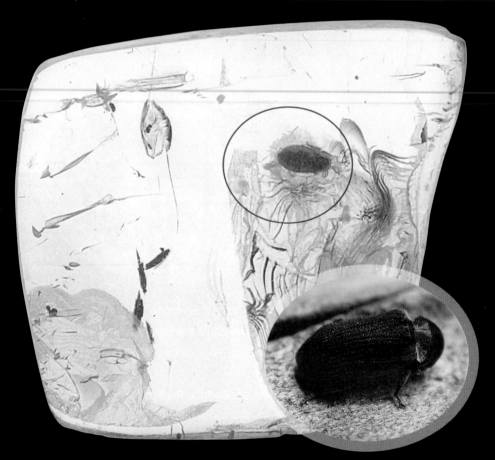

## Millipede

**Period: Eocene**

**Age: 45 million years**

**Location: Russia**

Just as spiders have always existed as spiders and mosquitoes have always existed as mosquitoes, millipedes too have always existed as millipedes. The 45-millionyear- old fossil millipede pictured confirms this fact. In the face of innumerable living fossil specimens, the theory of evolution is now due to be consigned to the dusty pages of history.

This has been recognized and understood by masses of people. But for some ideological concerns, a handful of Darwinists close their eyes to facts.

## Ground Cricket

**Period: Cretaceous**

**Age: 125 million years**

**Location: Brazil**

Asked about the origin of insects, Darwinists relate a series of hypotheses totally devoid of any logic. Asked to prove these stories with some scientific findings or concrete evidence, they enter into a profound silence—because all the theoretical studies to date, and findings such as fossils, completely invalidate these claims.

One of the pieces of evidence invalidating evolutionists' claims is the 125-million-year-old ground cricket fossil illustrated here. This fossilized insect, identical in every respect to ground crickets alive today, refutes evolutionist claims that living things are in a constant state of change. Fossils show that living things tell us, "We never changed or evolved. We were created."

The theory of evolution is entirely conjectural, devoid of any scientific criteria and based on no valid evidence. Moreover, it bases its entire claim on the illogical and unrealistic thesis that all living things in existence formed as the result of a succession of countless coincidences—something quite impossible.

Scientific research and investigations confirm this state of affairs. For example, examination of the fossil record shows that no process of the kind maintained by evolutionists ever happened. It can be seen that living things did not develop by way of a succession of changes, but that each one appeared suddenly with all its characteristics complete. This means that living things did not evolve, but were created.

**Spider**
Period: Cretaceous
Age: 125 million years
Location: Brazil

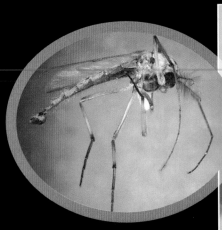

**Midge**

Period: Eocene

Age: 45 million years

Location: Russia

Darwinists—in a helpless position when it comes to the origin of insects, as they are with regard to so many other subjects— cannot offer any scientific explanation when confronted by fossils in amber. These life forms are manifest proofs that evolution never took place.

Male winged ants, or drones, are sent out from the colonies in order to mate with queens. There is no difference between this 25-million-year-old winged ant fossilized in the amber and present-day winged ants.

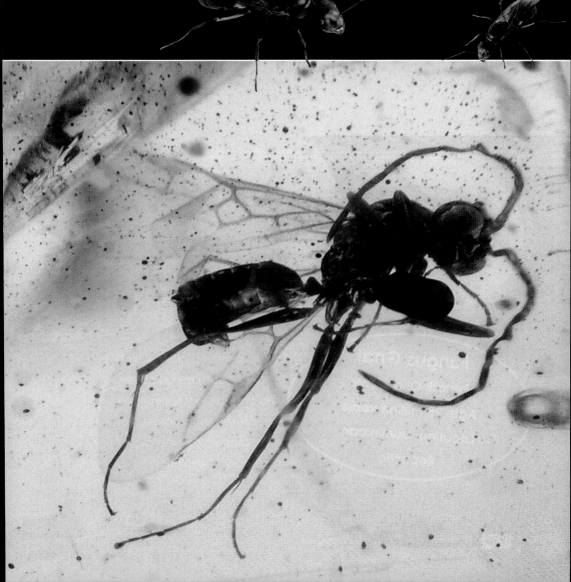

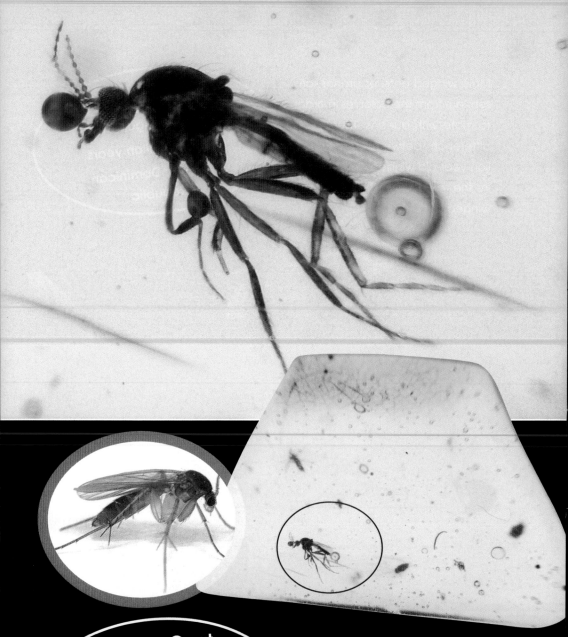

## Fungus Gnat

**Period: Oligocene**

**Age: 25 million years**

**Location: Dominican Republic**

The fossil in the picture, which shows that there had been no change in this life form's structure for millions of years, also refutes the claims of the theory of evolution.

Age: 54-37 million years

Location: USA

These beetles, which move on water by straddling the surface and supported by surface tension, have thin, long forelegs and hind legs. Water striders, which belong to Gerridae family, continuously smear the hairs on their feet and so they can stand on water without sinking. Those water striders that lived 54 to 37 million years ago were no different from those alive today. These beetles that have remained unchanged for tens of millions of years refute the Darwinists, who claim that the living species emerged through incremental changes. All living things were created by the Almighty God, Who created everything.

# Appendix

# The Deception
# of Evolution

*D*arwinism, in other words the theory of evolution, was put forward with the aim of denying the fact of Creation, but is in truth nothing but failed, unscientific nonsense. This theory, which claims that life emerged by chance from inanimate matter, was invalidated by the scientific evidence of miraculous order in the universe and in living things, as well as by the discovery of more than 300 million fossils revealing that evolution never happened. In this way, science confirmed the fact that God created the universe and the living things in it. The propaganda carried out today in order to keep the theory of evolution alive is based solely on the distortion of the scientific facts, biased interpretation, and lies and falsehoods disguised as science.

Yet this propaganda cannot conceal the truth. The fact that the theory of evolution is the greatest deception in the history of science has been expressed more and more in the scientific world over the last 20-30 years. Research carried out after the 1980s in particular has revealed that the claims of Darwinism are totally unfounded, something that has been stated by a large number of scientists. In the United States in particular, many scientists from such different fields as biology, biochemistry and paleontology recognize the invalidity of Darwinism and employ the fact of Creation to account for the origin of life.

We have examined the collapse of the theory of evolution and the proofs of Creation in great scientific detail in many of our works, and are still continuing to do so. Given the enormous importance of this subject, it will be of great benefit to summarize it here.

## The Scientific Collapse of Darwinism

As a pagan doctrine going back as far as ancient Greece, the theory of evolution was advanced most extensively in the nineteenth century. The most important development that made it the top topic of the world of science was

**Charles Darwin**

Charles Darwin's *The Origin of Species*, published in 1859. In this book, he opposed, in his own eyes, the fact that God created different living species on Earth separately, for he erroneously claimed that all living beings had a common ancestor and had diversified over time through small changes. Darwin's theory was not based on any concrete scientific finding; as he also accepted, it was just an "assumption." Moreover, as Darwin confessed in the long chapter of his book titled "Difficulties on Theory," the theory failed in the face of many critical questions.

Darwin invested all of his hopes in new scientific discoveries, which he expected to solve these difficulties. However, contrary to his expectations, scientific findings expanded the dimensions of these difficulties. The defeat of Darwinism in the face of science can be reviewed under three basic topics:

1) The theory cannot explain how life originated on Earth.

2) No scientific finding shows that the "evolutionary mechanisms" proposed by the theory have any evolutionary power at all.

3) The fossil record proves the exact opposite of what the theory suggests.

In this section, we will examine these three basic points in general outlines:

## The First Insurmountable Step: The Origin of Life

The theory of evolution posits that all living species evolved from a single living cell that emerged on Earth 3.8 billion years ago, supposed to have happened as a result of coincidences. How a single cell could generate millions of complex living species and, if such an evolution really occurred, why traces of it cannot be observed in the fossil record are some of the questions that the theory cannot answer. However, first and foremost, we need to ask: **How did this "first cell" originate?**

**Since the theory of evolution ignorantly denies Creation, it maintains that the "first cell" originated as a product of blind coincidences within the laws of nature, without any plan or arrangement.** According to the theory, inanimate matter must have produced a living cell as a result of coincidences. Such a claim, however, is inconsistent with the most unassailable rules of biology.

## "Life Comes From Life"

In his book, Darwin never referred to the origin of life. The primitive understanding of science in his time rested on the assumption that living beings had a very simple structure. Since medieval times, spontaneous generation, which asserts that non-living materials came together to form living organisms, had been widely accepted. It was commonly believed that insects came into being from food leftovers, and mice from wheat. Interesting experiments were conducted to prove this theory. Some wheat was placed on a dirty piece of cloth, and it was believed that mice would originate from it after a while.

Similarly, maggots developing in rotting meat was assumed to be evidence of spontaneous generation. However, **it was later understood that worms did not appear on meat spontaneously, but were carried there by flies in the form of larvae, invisible to the naked eye.**

Even when Darwin wrote *The Origin of Species*, the belief that bacteria could come into existence from non-living matter was widely accepted in the world of science.

However, **five years after the publication of Darwin's book, Louis Pasteur announced his results after long studies and experiments, that disproved spontaneous generation, a cornerstone of Darwin's theory.** In his triumphal lecture at the Sorbonne in 1864, **Pasteur said: "Never will the doctrine of spontaneous generation recover from the mortal blow struck by this simple experiment."** (Sidney Fox, Klaus Dose, *Molecular Evolution and The Origin of Life*, W. H. Freeman and Company, San Francisco, 1972, p. 4.)

For a long time, advocates of the theory

Louis Pasteur

of evolution resisted these findings. However, as the development of science unraveled the complex structure of the cell of a living being, the idea that life could come into being coincidentally faced an even greater impasse.

## Inconclusive Efforts of the Twentieth Century

The first evolutionist who took up the subject of the origin of life in the twentieth century was the renowned Russian biologist Alexander Oparin. With various theses he advanced in the 1930s, he tried to prove that a living cell could originate by coincidence. These studies, however, were doomed to failure, and Oparin had to make the following confession:

> *Unfortunately, however, the problem of the origin of the cell is perhaps the most obscure point in the whole study of the evolution of organisms. (Alexander I. Oparin, Origin of Life, Dover Publications, New York, 1936, 1953 (reprint), p. 196.)*

Evolutionist followers of Oparin tried to carry out experiments to solve this problem. The best known experiment was carried out by the American chemist Stanley Miller in 1953. Combining the gases he alleged to have existed in the primordial Earth's atmosphere in an experiment set-up, and adding energy to the mixture, Miller synthesized several organic molecules (amino acids) present in the structure of proteins.

Barely a few years had passed before it was revealed that **this experiment, which was**

**Alexandre Oparin**

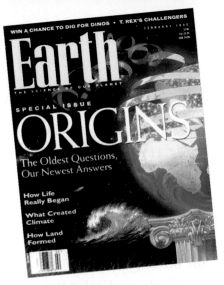

As accepted also by the latest evolutionist theorists, the origin of life is still a great stumbling block for the theory of evolution.

then presented as an important step in the name of evolution, was invalid, for the atmosphere used in the experiment was very different from the real Earth conditions. ("New Evidence on Evolution of Early Atmosphere and Life," *Bulletin of the American Meteorological Society*, vol 63, November 1982, 1328-1330)

After a long silence, **Miller confessed that the atmosphere medium he used was unrealistic.** (Stanley Miller, *Molecular Evolution of Life: Current Status of the Prebiotic Synthesis of Small Molecules*, 1986, p. 7)

**All the evolutionists' efforts throughout the twentieth century to explain the origin of life ended in failure.** The geochemist Jeffrey Bada, from the San Diego Scripps Institute accepts this fact in an article published in *Earth* magazine in 1998:

> *Today as we leave the twentieth century, we still face the biggest unsolved problem that we had when we entered the twentieth century: How did life originate on Earth? (Jeffrey Bada, Earth, February 1998, p. 40)*

## The Complex Structure of Life

The primary reason why evolutionists ended up in such a great impasse regarding the origin of life is that even those living organisms Darwinists deemed to be the simplest have outstandingly complex features. The cell of a living thing is more complex than all of our man-made technological products. **Today, even in the most developed laboratories of the world, no single protein of the cell,** let alone a living cell itself, can be produced by bringing organic chemicals together.

The conditions required for the formation of a cell are too great in quantity to be explained away by coincidences. However, there is no need to explain the situation with these details. Evolutionists are at a dead-end even before reaching the stage of the cell. That is because the probability of just a single protein, an essential building block of the cell, coming into being by chance is mathematically "0."

**The main reason for this is the need for other proteins to be present if one protein is to form, and this completely eradicates the possibility of chance formation. This fact by itself is sufficient to eliminate the evolutionist claim of chance right from the outset. To summarize,**

**1. Protein cannot be synthesized without enzymes, and enzymes are all proteins.**

**2. Around 100 proteins need to be present in order for a single protein to be synthesized. There therefore need to be proteins for proteins to exist.**

**3. DNA manufactures the protein-synthesizing enzymes. Protein cannot be synthesized without DNA. DNA is therefore also needed in order for proteins to form.**

**4. All the organelles in the cell have important tasks in protein synthesis. In other words, in order for proteins to form a perfect and fully functioning cell needs to exist together with all its organelles.**

The DNA molecule, which is located in the nucleus of a cell and which stores genetic information, is a magnificent databank. If the information coded in DNA were written down, it would make a giant library consisting of an estimated 900 volumes of encyclopedias consisting of 500 pages each.

A very interesting dilemma emerges at this point: DNA can replicate itself only with the help of some specialized proteins

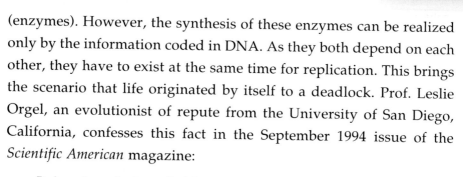

One of the facts nullifying the theory of evolution is the astonishingly complex structure of life. The DNA molecule located in the nucleus of cells of living beings is an example of this. The DNA is a sort of databank formed of the arrangement of four different molecules in different sequences. This databank contains the codes of all the physical traits of that living being. When the human DNA is put into writing, it is calculated that this would result in an encyclopedia made up of 900 volumes. Unquestionably, such extraordinary information definitively refutes the concept of coincidence.

(enzymes). However, the synthesis of these enzymes can be realized only by the information coded in DNA. As they both depend on each other, they have to exist at the same time for replication. This brings the scenario that life originated by itself to a deadlock. Prof. Leslie Orgel, an evolutionist of repute from the University of San Diego, California, confesses this fact in the September 1994 issue of the *Scientific American* magazine:

> *It is extremely improbable that proteins and nucleic acids, both of which are structurally complex, arose spontaneously in the same place at the same time.* Yet *it also seems impossible to have one without the other. And so, at first glance, one might have to conclude that life could never, in fact, have originated by chemical means.* (Leslie E. Orgel, "The Origin of Life on Earth," Scientific American, vol. 271, October 1994, p. 78.)

No doubt, if it is impossible for life to have originated spontaneously as a result of blind coincidences, then it has to be accepted that life was **created**. This fact explicitly invalidates the theory of evolution, whose main purpose is to deny Creation.

## Imaginary Mechanism of Evolution

The second important point that negates Darwin's theory is that both concepts put forward by the theory as "evolutionary mechanisms" were understood to have, in reality, no evolutionary power.

Darwin based his evolution allegation entirely on the mechanism of "natural selection." The importance he placed on this mechanism was evident in the name of his book: *The Origin of Species, By Means of Natural Selection...*

Natural selection holds that those living things that are stronger and more suited to the natural conditions of their habitats will survive in the struggle for life. For example, in a deer herd under the threat of attack by wild animals, those that can run faster will survive. Therefore, the deer herd will be comprised of faster and stronger individuals. However, unquestionably, this mechanism will not cause deer to evolve and transform themselves into another living species, for instance, horses.

Therefore, the mechanism of natural selection has no evolutionary power. Darwin was also aware of this fact and had to state this in his book *The Origin of Species*:

> *Natural selection can do nothing until favourable individual differences or variations occur. (Charles Darwin, The Origin of Species by Means of Natural Selection, The Modern Library, New York, p. 127)*

## Lamarck's Impact

So, how could these "favourable variations" occur? Darwin tried to answer this question from the standpoint of the primitive understanding of science at that time. According to the French biologist Chevalier de Lamarck (1744-1829), who lived before Darwin, living creatures passed on the traits they acquired during their lifetime to

the next generation. He asserted that these traits, which accumulated from one generation to another, caused new species to be formed. For instance, he claimed that giraffes evolved from antelopes; as they struggled to eat the leaves of high trees, their necks were extended from generation to generation.

Darwin also gave similar examples. In his book *The Origin of Species*, for instance, he said that some bears going into water to find food transformed themselves into whales over time. (Charles Darwin, *The Origin of Species: A Facsimile of the First Edition*, Harvard University Press, 1964, p. 184.)

However, the laws of inheritance discovered by Gregor Mendel (1822-84) and verified by the science of genetics, which flourished in the twentieth century, utterly demolished the legend that acquired traits were passed on to subsequent generations. Thus, natural selection fell out of favor as an evolutionary mechanism.

## Neo-Darwinism and Mutations

In order to find a solution, Darwinists advanced the "Modern Synthetic Theory," or as it is more commonly known, Neo-Darwinism, at the end of the 1930s. Neo-Darwinism added mutations, which are distortions formed in the genes of living beings due to such external factors as radiation or replication errors, as the "cause of favourable variations" in addition to natural mutation.

Today, the model that Darwinists espouse, despite their own awareness of its scientific invalidity, is neo-Darwinism. The theory maintains that millions of living beings formed as a result of a process whereby numerous complex organs of these organisms (e.g., ears, eyes, lungs, and wings) underwent "mutations," that is, genetic disorders. Yet, there is an outright scientific fact that totally undermines this theory: **Mutations do not cause living beings to develop; on the contrary, they are always harmful.**

The reason for this is very simple: **DNA has a very complex structure, and random effects can only harm it.** The American geneticist B. G. Ranganathan explains this as follows:

> First, genuine mutations are very rare in nature. Secondly, most mutations are harmful since they are random, rather than orderly changes in the structure of genes; any random change in a highly ordered system will be for the worse, not for the better. For example, *if an earthquake were to shake a highly ordered structure such as a building, there would be a random change in the framework of the building which, in all probability, would not be an improvement.* (B. G. Ranganathan, Origins?, Pennsylvania: The Banner of Truth Trust, 1988, p. 7.)

Not surprisingly, no mutation example, which is useful, that is, which is observed to develop the genetic code, has been observed so far. All mutations have proved to be harmful. It was understood that mutation, which is presented as an "evolutionary mechanism," is actually a genetic occurrence that harms living things, and leaves them disabled. (The most common effect of mutation on human

Since the beginning of the twentieth century, evolutionary biologists have sought examples of beneficial mutations by creating mutant flies. But these efforts have always resulted in sick and deformed creatures. The picture on the left shows the head of a normal fruit fly, and the picture on the right shows the head of a fruit fly with legs coming out of it, the result of mutation.

beings is cancer.) Of course, a destructive mechanism cannot be an "evolutionary mechanism." Natural selection, on the other hand, "can do nothing by itself," as Darwin also accepted. This fact shows us that **there is no "evolutionary mechanism" in nature.** Since no evolutionary mechanism exists, no such imaginary process called "evolution" could have taken place.

## The Fossil Record: No Sign of Intermediate Forms

The clearest evidence that the scenario suggested by the theory of evolution did not take place is the fossil record.

According to the unscientific supposition of this theory, every living species has sprung from a predecessor. A previously existing species turned into something else over time and all species have come into being in this way. In other words, this transformation proceeds gradually over millions of years.

*Adnan Oktar (Harun Yahya)*   **271**

Had this been the case, numerous intermediary species should have existed and lived within this long transformation period.

For instance, some half-fish/half-reptiles should have lived in the past which had acquired some reptilian traits in addition to the fish traits they already had. Or there should have existed some reptile-birds, which acquired some bird traits in addition to the reptilian traits they already had. Since these would be in a transitional phase, they should be disabled, defective, crippled living beings. Evolutionists refer to these imaginary creatures, which they believe to have lived in the past, as "transitional forms."

**If such animals ever really existed, there should be millions and even billions of them in number and variety. More importantly, the remains of these strange creatures should be present in the fossil record.** In *The Origin of Species*, Darwin explained:

> *If my theory be true, numberless intermediate varieties, linking most closely all of the species of the same group together must assuredly have existed... Consequently, evidence of their former existence could be found only amongst fossil remains. (Charles Darwin, The Origin of Species: A Facsimile of the First Edition, p. 179)*

However, **Darwin was well aware that no fossils of these intermediate forms had yet been found.** He regarded this as a major difficulty for his theory. In one chapter of his book titled "Difficulties on Theory," he wrote:

> *Why, if species have descended from other species by insensibly fine gradations,* ***do we not everywhere see innumerable transitional forms? Why is not all nature in confusion instead of the species being, as we see them, well defined?... But, as by this theory innumerable transitional forms must have existed, why do we not find them embedded in countless numbers in the crust of the earth?... Why then is not every geological formation and every stratum full of such intermediate links?*** *(Charles Darwin, The Origin of Species, p. 172)*

This fossil crocodile from the Cretaceous period is 65 million years old. It is identical to crocodiles living today.

This mene unearthed in Italy is 54 to 37 million years old.

This 50-million-year-old fossil plane-tree leaf was unearthed in the USA. Plane-tree leaves have remained unchanged for 50 million years, and have never evolved.

## Darwin's Hopes Shattered

However, although evolutionists have been making strenuous efforts to find fossils since the middle of the nineteenth century all over the world, **no transitional forms have yet been uncovered.** All of the fossils, contrary to the evolutionists' expectations, show that **life appeared on Earth all of a sudden and fully-formed.**

One famous British paleontologist, Derek V. Ager, admits this fact, even though he is an evolutionist:

> *The point emerges that if we examine the fossil record in detail, whether at the level of orders or of species, **we find – over and over again – not gradual evolution, but the sudden explosion of one group at the expense of another.** (Derek A. Ager, "The Nature of the Fossil Record," Proceedings of the British Geological Association, vol 87, 1976, p. 133.)*

This means that in **the fossil record, all living species suddenly emerge as fully formed, without any intermediate forms in between.** This is just the opposite of Darwin's assumptions. Also, this is very strong evidence that **all living things are created**. The only explanation of a living species emerging suddenly and complete in every detail without any evolutionary ancestor is that it was created. This fact is admitted also by the widely known evolutionist biologist Douglas Futuyma:

> *Creation and evolution, between them, exhaust the possible explanations for the origin of living things. Organisms either appeared on the earth fully developed or they did not. If they did not, they must have developed from pre-existing species by some process of modification. If they did appear in a fully developed state, they must indeed have been created by some omnipotent intelligence. (Douglas J. Futuyma, Science on Trial, Pantheon Books, New York, 1983, p. 197)*

**Fossils show that living beings emerged fully developed and**

**in a perfect state on the Earth**. That means that "the origin of species," contrary to Darwin's supposition, is not evolution, but Creation.

## The Tale of Human Evolution

The subject most often brought up by advocates of the theory of evolution is the subject of the origin of man. The Darwinist claim holds that man evolved from so-called ape-like creatures. During this alleged evolutionary process, which is supposed to have started four to five million years ago, some "transitional forms" between man and his imaginary ancestors are supposed to have existed. According to this completely imaginary scenario, four basic "categories" are listed:

1. *Australopithecus*
2. *Homo habilis*
3. *Homo erectus*
4. *Homo sapiens*

Evolutionists call man's so-called first ape-like ancestors *Australopithecus*, which means "South African ape." These living beings are actually nothing but an old ape species that has become extinct. Extensive research done on various *Australopithecus* specimens by two world famous anatomists from England and the USA, namely, Lord Solly Zuckerman and Prof. Charles Oxnard, shows that these apes belonged to an ordinary ape species that became extinct and bore no resemblance to humans. (Solly Zuckerman, *Beyond The Ivory Tower*, Toplinger Publications, New York, 1970, 75-14; Charles E. Oxnard, "The Place of Australopithecines in Human Evolution: Grounds for Doubt", Nature, vol 258, 389)

Evolutionists classify the next stage of human evolution as "homo," that is "man." According to their claim, the living beings in the Homo series are more developed than *Australopithecus*. Evolutionists devise a fanciful evolution scheme by arranging different fossils of these creatures in a particular order. This scheme is imaginary because it has never been proved that there is an evolutionary relation between these different classes. Ernst Mayr, one of the twentieth century's most important evolutionists, contends in his book *One Long Argument* that "particularly historical [puzzles] such as the origin of life or of Homo sapiens, are extremely difficult and may even resist a final, satisfying explanation." ("Could science be brought to an end by scientists' belief that they have final answers or by society's reluctance to pay the bills?" *Scientific American*, December 1992, p. 20)

By outlining the link chain as *Australopithecus* > *Homo habilis* > *Homo erectus* > *Homo sapiens*, evolutionists imply that each of these species is one another's ancestor. However, recent findings of paleoanthropologists have revealed that *Australopithecus*, *Homo habilis*, and *Homo erectus* lived at different parts of the world at the same

There are no fossil remains that support the tale of human evolution. On the contrary, the fossil record shows that there is an insurmountable barrier between apes and men. In the face of this truth, evolutionists fixed their hopes on certain drawings and models. They randomly place masks on the fossil remains and fabricate imaginary half-ape, half-human faces.

time. (Alan Walker, *Science*, vol. 207, 7 March 1980, p. 1103; A. J. Kelso, *Physical Antropology*, 1st ed., J. B. Lipincott Co., New York, 1970, p. 221; M. D. Leakey, *Olduvai Gorge*, vol. 3, Cambridge University Press, Cambridge, 1971, p. 272.)

Moreover, a certain segment of humans classified as *Homo erectus* have lived up until very modern times. **Homo sapiens neandarthalensis and Homo sapiens sapiens (man) co-existed in the same region.** (Jeffrey Kluger, "Not So Extinct After All: The Primitive Homo Erectus May Have Survived Long Enough To Coexist With Modern Humans," *Time*, 23 December 1996)

This situation apparently indicates the invalidity of the claim that they are ancestors of one another. The late Stephen Jay Gould explained this deadlock of the theory of evolution although he was himself one of the leading advocates of evolution in the twentieth century:

> *What has become of our ladder if there are three coexisting lineages of hominids (A. africanus, the robust australopithecines, and H. habilis), none clearly derived from another? Moreover, none of the three display any evolutionary trends during their tenure on earth.* (S. J. Gould, *Natural History*, vol. 85, 1976, p. 30)

Put briefly, the scenario of human evolution, which is "upheld" with the help of various drawings of some "half ape, half human" creatures appearing in the media and course books, that is, frankly, by means of propaganda, is nothing but **a tale with no scientific foundation.**

Lord Solly Zuckerman, one of the most famous and respected scientists in the U.K., who carried out research on this subject for years and studied Australopithecus fossils for 15 years, finally concluded, despite being an evolutionist himself, **that there is, in fact, no such family tree branching out from ape-like creatures to man.**

Zuckerman also made an interesting "spectrum of science" rang-

Can life emerge if all the conditions stipulated by evolutionists are met? Of course not! In order to show why not, let us carry out the following experiment: Place all the enzymes, hormones and proteins—everything that evolutionists regard as essential for life to form—into a barrel such as that pictured above. Then mix all these substances, using all possible physical and chemical techniques. But whatever you do, no matter how long you wait, not a single living cell will emerge from that barrel.

ing from those he considered scientific to those he considered unscientific. According to Zuckerman's spectrum, the most "scientific"—that is, depending on concrete data—fields of science are chemistry and physics. After them come the biological sciences and then the social sciences. At the far end of the spectrum, which is the part considered to be most "unscientific," are "extra-sensory perception"—concepts such as telepathy and sixth sense—and finally "human evolution." Zuckerman explains his reasoning:

> We then move right off the register of objective truth into those fields of presumed biological science, like extrasensory perception or the interpretation of man's fossil history, where to the faithful [evolutionist] anything is possible – and where the ardent believer [in evolution] is sometimes able to believe several contradictory things at the same time. (Solly Zuckerman, Beyond the Ivory Tower, p. 19)

**The tale of human evolution** boils down to nothing but the prejudiced interpretations of some fossils unearthed by certain people, who blindly adhere to their theory.

## Darwinian Formula!

Besides all the technical evidence we have dealt with so far, let us now for once, examine what kind of a superstition the evolutionists have with an example so simple as to be understood even by children:

The theory of evolution asserts that life is formed by chance. According to this irrational claim, lifeless and unconscious atoms came together to form the cell and then they somehow formed other living things, including man. Let us think about that. When we bring together the elements that are the building-blocks of life such as carbon, phosphorus, nitrogen and potassium, only a heap is formed. No matter what treatments it undergoes, this atomic heap cannot form even a single living being. If you like, let us formulate an "experiment" on this subject and let us examine on the behalf of evolutionists what they really claim without pronouncing loudly under the name **"Darwinian formula"**:

Let evolutionists put plenty of materials present in the composition of living things such as phosphorus, nitrogen, carbon, oxygen, iron, and magnesium into big barrels. Moreover, let them add in these barrels any material that does not exist under normal conditions, but they think as necessary. Let them add in this mixture as many amino acids and as many proteins - a single one of which can by no means form by chance - as they like. Let them expose these mixtures to as much heat and moisture as they like. Let them stir these with whatever technologically developed device they like. Let them put the foremost scientists beside these barrels. Let these experts wait in turn beside these barrels for billions, and even trillions of years. Let them be free to use all kinds of conditions they believe to be necessary for a human's formation. **No matter what they do,**

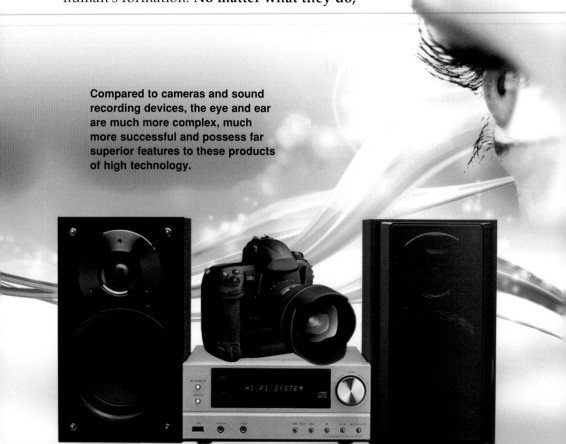

Compared to cameras and sound recording devices, the eye and ear are much more complex, much more successful and possess far superior features to these products of high technology.

they cannot produce from these barrels a human, say a professor that examines his cell structure under the electron microscope. They cannot produce giraffes, lions, bees, canaries, horses, dolphins, roses, orchids, lilies, carnations, bananas, oranges, apples, dates, tomatoes, melons, watermelons, figs, olives, grapes, peaches, peafowls, pheasants, multicoloured butterflies, or millions of other living beings such as these. Indeed, they could not obtain even a single cell of any one of them.

Briefly, **unconscious atoms cannot form the cell** by coming together. They cannot take a new decision and divide this cell into two, then take other decisions and create the professors who first invent the electron microscope and then examine their own cell structure under that microscope. **Matter is an unconscious, lifeless heap, and it comes to life with God's superior creation.**

The theory of evolution, which claims the opposite, is a total fallacy completely contrary to reason. Thinking even a little bit on the claims of evolutionists discloses this reality, just as in the above example.

## Technology in the Eye and the Ear

Another subject that remains unanswered by evolutionary theory is the excellent quality of perception in the eye and the ear.

Before passing on to the subject of the eye, let us briefly answer the question of how we see. Light rays coming from an object fall oppositely on the eye's retina. Here, these light rays are transmitted into electric signals by cells and reach a tiny spot at the back of the brain, the "center of vision." These electric signals are perceived in this center as an image after a series of processes. With this technical background, let us do some thinking.

**The brain is insulated from light.** That means that its inside is completely dark, and that no light reaches the place where it is located. Thus, the "center of vision" is never touched by light and may even be the darkest place you have ever known. However, you observe a luminous, bright world in this pitch darkness.

**The image formed in the eye is so sharp and distinct that even the technology of the twentieth century has not been able to attain it.** For instance, look at the book you are reading, your hands with which you are holding it, and then lift your head and look around you. Have you ever seen such a sharp and distinct image as this one at any other place? Even the most developed television screen produced by the greatest television producer in the world cannot provide such a sharp image for you. This is a three-dimensional, colored, and extremely sharp image. For more than 100 years, thousands of engineers have been trying to achieve this sharpness. Factories, huge premises were established, much research has been done, plans and designs have been made for this purpose. Again, look at a TV screen

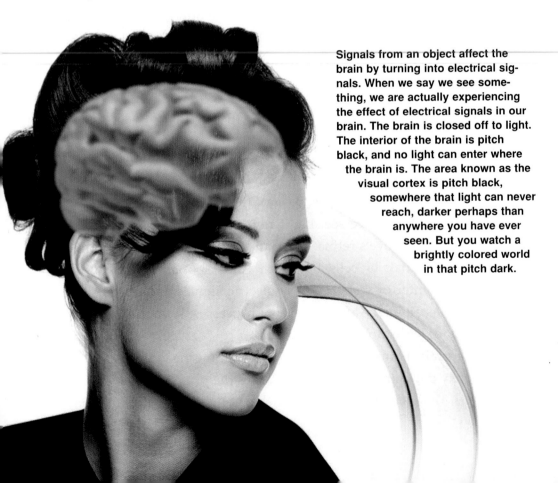

Signals from an object affect the brain by turning into electrical signals. When we say we see something, we are actually experiencing the effect of electrical signals in our brain. The brain is closed off to light. The interior of the brain is pitch black, and no light can enter where the brain is. The area known as the visual cortex is pitch black, somewhere that light can never reach, darker perhaps than anywhere you have ever seen. But you watch a brightly colored world in that pitch dark.

and the book you hold in your hands. You will see that there is a big difference in sharpness and distinction. Moreover, the TV screen shows you a two-dimensional image, whereas with your eyes, you watch a three-dimensional perspective with depth.

For many years, tens of thousands of engineers have tried to make a three-dimensional TV and achieve the vision quality of the eye. Yes, they have made a three-dimensional television system, but it is not possible to watch it without putting on special 3-D glasses; moreover, it is only an artificial three-dimension. The background is more blurred, the foreground appears like a paper setting. Never has it been possible to produce a sharp and distinct vision like that of the eye. In both the camera and the television, there is a loss of image quality.

Evolutionists claim that the mechanism producing this sharp and distinct image has been formed by chance. Now, if somebody told you that the television in your room was formed as a result of chance, that all of its atoms just happened to come together and make up this device that produces an image, what would you think? How can atoms do what thousands of people cannot?

If a device producing a more primitive image than **the eye could not have been formed by chance**, then it is very evident that the eye and the image seen by the eye could not have been formed by chance. The same situation applies to the ear. The outer ear picks up the available sounds by the auricle and directs them to the middle ear, the middle ear transmits the sound vibrations by intensifying them, and the inner ear sends these vibrations to the brain by translating them into electric signals. Just as with the eye, the act of hearing finalizes in the center of hearing in the brain.

The situation in the eye is also true for the ear. That is, **the brain is insulated from sound** just as it is from light. It does not let any sound in. Therefore, no matter how noisy is the outside, the inside of the brain is completely silent. Nevertheless, the sharpest sounds are perceived in the brain. In **your completely silent brain, you listen to symphonies, and hear all of the noises in a crowded place.** However, were the sound level in your brain measured by a precise device at that moment, complete silence would be found to be prevailing there.

As is the case with imagery, decades of effort have been spent in trying to generate and reproduce sound that is faithful to the original. The results of these efforts are sound recorders, high-fidelity systems, and systems for sensing sound. Despite all of this technology and the thousands of engineers and experts who have been working on this endeavor, no sound has yet been obtained that has the same sharpness and clarity as the sound perceived by the ear. Think of the highest-quality hi-fi systems produced by the largest company in the music industry. Even in these devices, when sound is recorded some of it is lost; or when you turn on a hi-fi you always hear a hissing sound before the music starts. However, the sounds that are the products of the human body's technology are extremely sharp and clear. A human ear never perceives a sound accompanied by a hissing sound or with atmospherics as does a hi-fi; rather, it perceives sound exactly as it is, sharp and clear. This is the way it has been since **the creation of man.**

So far, no man-made visual or recording apparatus has been as sensitive and successful in perceiving sensory data as are the eye and the ear. However, as far as seeing and hearing are concerned, a far greater truth lies beyond all this.

## To Whom Does the Consciousness that Sees and Hears within the Brain Belong?

Who watches an alluring world in the brain, listens to symphonies and the twittering of birds, and smells the rose?

The stimulations coming from a person's eyes, ears, and nose travel to the brain as electro-chemical nerve impulses. In biology, physiology, and biochemistry books, you can find many details about how this image forms in the brain. However, you will never come across the most important fact: Who perceives these electro-chemical nerve impulses as images, sounds, odors, and sensory events in the brain? **There is a consciousness in the brain that perceives all this without feeling any need for an eye, an ear, and a nose.** To whom does this consciousness belong? Of course it does not belong to the nerves, the fat layer, and neurons comprising the brain. This is why Darwinist-materialists, who believe that everything is comprised of matter, cannot answer these questions.

For **this consciousness is the spirit created by God**, which needs neither the eye to watch the images nor the ear to hear the sounds. Furthermore, it does not need the brain to think.

Everyone who reads this explicit and scientific fact should ponder on Almighty God, and fear and seek refuge in Him, for He squeezes the entire universe in a pitch-dark place of a few cubic centimeters in a three-dimensional, colored, shadowy, and luminous form.

## A Materialist Faith

The information we have presented so far shows us that **the theory of evolution is incompatible with scientific findings.** The theory's claim regarding the origin of life is inconsistent with science, the evolutionary mechanisms it proposes have no evolutionary power, and fossils demonstrate that **the required intermediate forms have never existed.** So, it certainly follows that the theory of evolution should be pushed aside as an unscientific idea. This is how many ideas, such as the Earth-centered universe model, have been taken out of the agenda of science throughout history.

However, the theory of evolution is kept on the agenda of science. Some people even try to represent criticisms directed against it as an "attack on science." Why?

The reason is that this theory is an indispensable dogmatic belief for some circles. These circles are **blindly devoted** to materialist philosophy and adopt Darwinism because it is the only materialist explanation that can be put forward to explain the workings of nature.

Interestingly enough, they also confess this fact from time to time. A well-known geneticist and an outspoken evolutionist, Richard C. Lewontin from Harvard University, confesses that he is "first and foremost a materialist and then a scientist":

> *It is not that the methods and institutions of science somehow compel us accept a material explanation of the phenomenal world, but, on the contrary, that we are forced by our a priori adherence to material causes to create an apparatus of investigation and a set of concepts that produce material explanations, no matter how counter-intuitive, no matter how mystifying to the uninitiated. Moreover, that materialism is absolute, so we cannot allow a Divine [intervention]...(Richard Lewontin, "The Demon-Haunted World," The New York Review of Books, January 9, 1997, p. 28)*

These are explicit statements that **Darwinism is a dogma** kept alive just for the sake of adherence to materialism. This dogma maintains that there is no being save matter. Therefore, it argues that inanimate, unconscious matter brought life into being. It insists that millions of different living species (e.g., birds, fish, giraffes, tigers, insects, trees, flowers, whales, and human beings) originated as a result of the interactions between matter such as pouring rain, lightning flashes, and so on, out of inanimate matter. This is a precept contrary both to reason and science. Yet Darwinists continue to ignorantly defend it just so as not to acknowledge, in their own eyes, the evident existence of God.

Anyone who does not look at the origin of living beings with a materialist prejudice sees this evident truth: **All living beings are works of a Creator,** Who is All-Powerful, All-Wise, and All-Knowing. **This Creator is God,** Who created the whole universe from non-existence, in the most perfect form, and fashioned all living beings.

## The Theory of Evolution: The Most Potent Spell in the World

Anyone free of prejudice and the influence of any particular ideology, who uses only his or her reason and logic, will clearly understand that belief in the theory of evolution, which brings to mind the superstitions of societies with no knowledge of science or civilization, is quite impossible.

As explained above, those who believe in the theory of evolution think that a few atoms and molecules thrown into a huge vat could produce thinking, reasoning professors and university students; such scientists as Einstein and Galileo; such artists as Humphrey Bogart, Frank Sinatra and Luciano Pavarotti; as well as antelopes, lemon trees, and carnations. Moreover, as the scientists and professors who believe in this nonsense are educated people, it is quite justifiable to speak of this theory as "the most potent spell in history." Never before has any other belief or idea so taken away peoples' powers of reason, refused to allow them to think intelligently and logically, and hidden the truth from them as if they had been blindfolded. This is an even worse and unbelievable blindness than the totem worship in some parts of Africa, the people of Saba worshipping the Sun, the tribe of the Prophet Abraham (pbuh) worshipping idols they had made with their own hands, or some among the people of the Prophet Moses (pbuh) worshipping the Golden Calf.

In fact, God has pointed to this lack of reason in the Qur'an. In many verses, He reveals that some peoples' minds will be closed and that they will be powerless to see the truth. Some of these verses are as follows:

**As for those who do not believe, it makes no difference to them whether you warn them or do not warn them, they will not believe.**

God has sealed up their hearts and hearing and over their eyes is a blindfold. They will have a terrible punishment. (Qur'an, 2:6-7)

... They have hearts with which they do not understand. They have eyes with which they do not see. They have ears with which they do not hear. Such people are like cattle. No, they are even further astray! They are the unaware. (Qur'an, 7:179)

Even if We opened up to them a door into heaven, and they spent the day ascending through it, they would only say: "Our eyesight is befuddled! Or rather we have been put under a spell!" (Qur'an, 15:14-15)

Words cannot express just how astonishing it is that this spell should hold such a wide community in thrall, keep people from the truth, and not be broken for 150 years. It is understandable that one or a few people might believe in impossible scenarios and claims full of stupidity and illogicality. However, "magic" is the only possible explanation for people from all over the world believing that unconscious and lifeless atoms suddenly decided to come together and form a universe that functions with a flawless system of organization, discipline, reason, and consciousness; a planet named Earth with all of its features so perfectly suited to life; and living things full of countless complex systems.

In fact, in the Qur'an God relates the incident of the Prophet Moses (pbuh) and Pharaoh to show that some people who support atheistic philosophies actually influence others by magic. When Pharaoh was told about the true religion, he told the Prophet Moses (pbuh) to meet with his own magicians. When the Prophet Moses (pbuh) did so, he told them to demonstrate their abilities first. The verses continue:

He said: "You throw." And when they threw, they cast a spell on the people's eyes and caused them to feel great fear of them. They produced an extremely powerful magic. (Qur'an, 7:116)

As we have seen, Pharaoh's magicians were able to deceive everyone, apart from the Prophet Moses (pbuh) and those who believed in him. However, his evidence broke the spell, or "swallowed up what they had forged," as revealed in the verse:

**We revealed to Moses: "Throw down your staff." And it immediately swallowed up what they had forged. So the Truth took place and what they did was shown to be false. (Qur'an, 7:117-118)**

As we can see, when people realized that a spell had been cast upon them and that what they saw was just an illusion, Pharaoh's magicians lost all credibility. In the present day too, unless those who, under the influence of a similar spell, believe in these ridiculous claims under their scientific disguise and spend their lives defending them, abandon their superstitious beliefs, they also will be humiliated when the full truth emerges and the spell is broken. In fact, worldrenowned British writer and philosopher Malcolm Muggeridge, who was an atheist defending evolution for some sixty years, but

In the same way that the beliefs of people who worshipped crocodiles now seem odd and unbelievable, so the beliefs of Darwinists are just as incredible. Darwinists regard chance and lifeless, unconscious atoms as a creative force, and are as devoted to that belief as if to a religion.

who subsequently realized the truth, reveals the position in which the theory of evolution would find itself in the near future in these terms:

> *I myself am convinced that **the theory of evolution**, especially the extent to which it's been applied, **will be one of the great jokes in the history books in the future.** Posterity will marvel that so very flimsy and dubious an hypothesis could be accepted with the incredible credulity that it has. (Malcolm Muggeridge, The End of Christendom, Grand Rapids: Eerdmans, 1980, p. 43)*

That future is not far off: On the contrary, people will soon see that "chance" is not a deity, and will look back on **the theory of evolution as the worst deceit and the most terrible spell in the world.** That spell is already rapidly beginning to be lifted from the shoulders of people all over the world. Many people who see its true face are wondering with amazement how they could ever have been taken in by it.

# WHO SEES?

From the moment a person is born, he becomes subject to the steady indoctrination of the society. Part of this indoctrination, possibly the most persuasive, holds that reality is what the hands can touch and the eyes can see. This understanding, which is quite influential in the majority of the society, is carried without question from one generation to another.

But without being subjected to any indoctrination, a moment of objective thought would make one realize an astonishing fact:

Everything we confront from the moment we come into existence—human beings, animals, flowers, their colors, odors, fruits, tastes of fruits, planets, stars, mountains, stones, buildings, space—are perceptions presented to us by our five senses. To further clarify this, it will help to examine the senses, the agents that provide us with information about the exterior world.

All of man's sensory faculties—sight, hearing, smell, taste and touch—function in the same way. Stimuli (lights, sounds, smells, tastes, textures) from objects in the external world are carried through nerves to the sensory centers in the brain. All these stimuli that reach the brain consist of electric signals. For example, during the process of vision, light rays (or photons) radiating from sources in the exterior world reach the retina at the back of the eye and, through a series of processes, are transformed into electric signals. These signals are transferred along nerves to the brain's vision center. There, a colorful, bright and three-dimensional world is perceived within the space of a few cubic centimeters.

The same system applies to other senses as well. Cells on the surface of the tongue transform chemical traces into electric signals that become tastes. Odors are transformed into electric signals by cells in the epithelium of the nose. Special sensors lodged beneath the skin transform impulses of touch (such as the sensations of hardness or softness) into electric signals, and a special mechanism in the ear does the same with sound. All these signals are sent to appropriate centers in the brain, where they are perceived.

To clarify the point, assume that you're drinking a glass of lemonade. The hard, cool surface of the glass you're holding is transformed into electric signals by special receptors under your skin and sent to the brain. Simultaneously, the smell of the lemonade, its taste, and yellowish color all become signals that reach the brain. Likewise, the clink you hear when the glass touches the table is perceived by the ear and transmitted to the brain as an electric signal. All these perceptions are interpreted in the brain's relevant centers, which work harmoniously with one another. As a cumulative result of these impulses, you sense that you are drinking a glass of lemonade.

Concerning this important fact, consider the thoughts of B. Russell and L. J. J. Wittgenstein, two famous philosophers:

> For instance, whether a lemon truly exists or not and how it came to exist cannot be questioned and investigated. A lemon consists merely of a taste sensed by the tongue, an odor sensed by the nose, a color and shape sensed by the eye; and only these features of it can be subject to examination and assessment. **Science can never know the physical world.** (*John L. Esposito, Islam : The Straight Path, p. 58*)

In other words, it is impossible for us to reach the physical world. All objects we're in contact with are actually collection of perceptions such as sight, hearing, and touch. Throughout our lives, by processing the data in the sensory centers, our brain **confronts not the "originals" of the matter existing outside us, but rather copies inside our brain**. At this point, we are misled to assume that these copies are instances of real matter outside us.

This obvious fact has been proven by science today. Any scientist

would tell you how this system works, and that the world we live in is really an aggregate of perceptions formed in our brains. The English physicist John Gribbin states that our senses are an interpretation of stimulations coming from the external world—as if there were a tree in the garden. He goes on to say that our brain perceives the stimulations that are filtered through our senses, and that the tree is only a stimulation. So, he then asks, which tree is real? The one formed by our senses, or the tree in the garden? *(Prof. Thomas Arnold, The Spread of Islam in the World, A History of Peaceful Preaching, p. 56)*

No doubt, this reality requires profound reflection. As a result of these physical facts, we come to the following indisputable conclusion: Everything we see, touch, hear, and call "matter," "the world" or "the universe" is nothing more than electrical signals interpreted in our brain. We can never reach the original of the matter outside our brain. We merely taste, hear and see an image of the external world formed in our brain.

In fact, someone eating an apple confronts not the actual fruit, but its perceptions in the brain. What that person considers to be an apple actually consists of his brain's perception of the electrical information concerning the fruit's shape, taste, smell, and texture. If the optic nerve to the brain were suddenly severed, the image of the fruit would instantly disappear. Any disconnection in the olfactory nerve traveling from receptors in the nose to the brain would interrupt the sense of smell completely. Simply put, that apple is nothing but the interpretation of electrical signals by the brain.

Also consider the sense of distance. The empty space between you and this page is only a sense of emptiness formed in your brain. Objects that appear distant in your view also exist in the brain. For instance, someone watching the stars at night assumes that they are millions of light-years away, yet the stars are within himself, in his vision center. While you read these lines, actually you are not inside the room you assume you're in; on the contrary, the room is inside you. Perceiving your body makes you think that you're inside it. **However, your body, too, is a set of images formed inside your brain.**

## Millions of Colors in a Pitch-Black Location

Considering this subject in greater detail reveals some even more extraordinary truths. Our sense centers are located in the brain, a three-pound piece of tissue. And this organ is protected inside an array of bones called the skull, which neither light, nor sound, nor odors can penetrate. The inside of the skull is a dark, silent place where all smells are absent.

But in this place of complete darkness occur millions of color shades and sound tones, as well countless different tastes and smells.

So how does this happen?

What makes you perceive light in a location without light, odors in a place without smell, sounds in total silence and the objects of all other senses? Who created all of this for you?

In every moment of your life, a variety of miracles take place. As mentioned earlier, anything your senses can detect in this room you're in, are sent as electrical signals to your brain, where they then combine. Your brain interprets them as a view of a room. Put another way, while you assume that you are sitting in this room, that room is actually inside you, in your brain. The "place" where the room is assembled and perceived is small, dark, and soundless. And yet a whole room or a whole landscape, regardless of its size, can fit into it. Both a narrow closet and a wide vista of the sea are perceived in the exact same place.

Our brains interpret and attribute meaning to the signals relating to the "external world." As an example, consider the sense of hearing. It's our brain that in fact interprets and transforms the sound waves into a symphony. That is to say, music is yet another perception created by our brain. In the same manner, when we perceive colors, what reaches our eyes is merely light of different wavelengths. Again, it's our brain that transforms these signals into colors. There are no colors in the "external world"; neither is an apple red, nor the sky blue, nor the leaves green. They appear as they do simply because we perceive them to be so.

Even a slight defect in the eye's retina can cause color blindness. Some sufferers perceive blue and green as the same, some red as blue. At this point, it does not matter whether or not the outside object is colored.

The prominent thinker George Berkeley also addresses this fact:

At the beginning, it was believed that colors, odors, etc., "really exist," but subsequently such views were renounced, and it was seen that they only exist in dependence on our sensations. *(John L. Esposito, Islam : The Straight Path, p. 59)*

In conclusion, the reason we see objects in colors is not because they are actually colored or have a material existence in the outer world. The truth, rather, is that the qualities we ascribe to objects are all inside us.

And this, perhaps, is a truth you have never considered before.

## Mankind's Limited Knowledge

One implication of the facts described so far is that actually, man's knowledge of the external world is exceedingly limited.

That knowledge is limited to our five senses, and there is no proof that the world we perceive by means of those senses is identical to the "real" world.

It may, therefore, be very different from what we perceive. There may be a great many dimensions and other beings of which we remain unaware. Even if we reach the furthermost extremities of the universe, our knowledge will always remain limited.

Almighty God, the Creator of all, has complete and flawless knowledge of all beings who, having been created by God, can possess only the

knowledge that He allows them. This fact is related in the Qur'an thus:

> **God, there is no god but Him, the Living, the Self-Sustaining. He is not subject to drowsiness or sleep. Everything in the heavens and the earth belongs to Him. Who can intercede with Him except by His permission? He knows what is before them and what is behind them but they cannot grasp any of His knowledge save what He wills. His Footstool encompasses the heavens and the Earth and their preservation does not tire Him. He is the Most High, the Magnificent. (Qur'an, 2: 255)**

## Who Is the Perceiver?

In order to perceive, no external world is necessary. Given the right kind of stimulation to the brain, sensations of touch, sight, and sounds, can be recreated in the brain. The best example of this process is dreams.

During dreams, your body typically remains still and motionless in a dark and quiet bedroom, and your eyes remain shut. Neither light nor sound nor any other stimuli from the exterior world is reaching your brain for it to perceive. Yet in your dreams, you still perceive experiences very

similar to real life. In your dreams you also get up and go to work, or go on vacation and enjoy the warmth of the sun.

Furthermore, in dreams you never feel doubts about the reality of what you experience. Only after you wake up you realize your experiences were only dreams. You not only experience such feelings as fear, anxiety, joy and sadness but also see different images, hear sounds and feel matter. Yet there is no physical source producing these sensations and perceptions; you lie motionless inside a dark and quiet room.

René Descartes, the renowned philosopher, offered the following reasoning on this surprising truth about dreams:

> In my dreams I see that I do various things, I go to many places; when I wake up, however, I see that I have not done anything or gone anywhere and that I lie peacefully in my bed. Who can guarantee to me that I do not also dream at the present time, further, that my whole life is not a dream?*(Karen Armstrong, Holy War, p. 185)*

We are therefore looking at a manifest truth: There is no justification for our claiming that we establish direct contact with the original of the world that we claim to exist and to be living in.

## Is Our Brain Distinct from the Outside World?

If everything we know as the outside world is only perceptions produced internally, what about the brain which we think does the seeing and hearing? Isn't it composed of atoms and molecules like everything else? The brain, too, is a piece of tissue that we perceive through our senses. This being so, what is it, if not the brain, that perceives everything—that sees, hears, touches, smells and tastes?

At this point, we face the obvious fact: that man, a being of consciousness who can see, feel, think and exercise reason, is much more than a mere assemblage of atoms and molecules. What defines a human being is the "soul" granted to him by God. Otherwise, it would be highly unreasonable to attribute his consciousness and other faculties to a three-pound piece of flesh:

> **He Who has created all things in the best possible way. He commenced the creation of man from clay; then produced his seed from an extract of base fluid; then formed him and breathed His Spirit into him and gave you hearing, sight and hearts. What little thanks you show! (Qur'an, 32: 7-9)**

## The Being Nearest to Us Is God

Since a human being is not merely a lump of matter but a "soul," then who makes that soul feel the sum of perceptions which we call the external world? Who continues to create all these perceptions, ceaselessly?

The answer is obvious. God, Who breathed into man His spirit, is the Creator of all things. He is also the real source of all perceptions. The existence of anything is possible only through God's creation. God informs us that He creates continuously and that whenever He stops creating, everything will disappear:

> **God keeps a firm hold on the heavens and the Earth, preventing them from vanishing away. And if they vanished no one could then keep hold of them. Certainly He is Most Forbearing, Ever-Forgiving. (Qur'an, 35: 41)**

This verse is describing how the material universe is maintained under the might of God. God created the universe, the Earth, mountains, and all living and non-living things, and maintains all these under His power at every moment. God manifests His name al-Khaliq in this material universe. God is al-Khaliq, in other words, the Creator of all things, the Creator from nothing. This shows that there is a material universe, outside our brains, consisting of entities created by God. However, as a miracle and manifestation of the superior nature of His creation and His omniscience, God shows us this material universe in the form of an "illusion," "shadow," or "image." As a consequence of the perfection in His creation, human beings can never reach the world outside their brains. Only God knows this real material universe.

Another interpretation of the above verse is that God constantly maintains the images of the material universe that people see. (God knows best.) If God wished not to show us the image of the world in our minds, the entire universe would disappear for us, and we could never again make contact with it.

Faced with such facts, one must conclude that the only absolute being is God, Who encompasses everything in the heavens and the Earth:

**What! Are they in doubt about the meeting with their Lord? What! Does He not encompass all things! (Qur'an, 41: 54)**

**Both East and West belong to God, so wherever you turn, the Face of God is there. God is All-Encompassing, All-Knowing. (Qur'an, 2: 115)**

**What is in the heavens and in the Earth belongs to God. God encompasses all things. (Qur'an, 4: 126)**

**When We said to you, "Surely your Lord encompasses the people with His knowledge"... (Qur'an, 17: 60)**

**... His Footstool encompasses the heavens and the Earth and their preservation does not tire Him. He is the Most High, the Magnificent. (Qur'an, 2: 255)**

God's knowledge and ability surrounds us from the front and back, from right and left—that is to say, He encompasses us completely. He

## Notes:

1. Peter Douglas Ward, *On Methuselah's Trail*, W. H. Freedman and Company, 1992, p. 9
2. Stephen J. Gould, *The Panda's Thumb*, 1980, pp. 238-239
3. N. Eldredge et I. Tattersall, *The Myths of Human Evolution*, Columbia University Press, 1982, pp. 45-46
4. David Raup, "Conflicts Between Darwin and Paleontology", *Field Museum of Natural History Bulletin*, Field Museum of Natural History: Chicago IL, January 1979, vol. 50, no. 1, pp. 22-29
5. D.S. Woodroff, *Science*, vol. 208, 1980, p. 716
6. George G., Simpson, *Tempo and Mode in Evolution*, Columbia University Press, New York, 1944, pp. 105, 107
7. Charles Darwin, *L'origine des espèces*, GF Flammarion, Paris, 1992, pp. 223, 225, 334
8. Derek A. Ager, "The Nature of the Fossil Record", *Proceedings of the British Geological Association*, vol. 87, 1976, p. 133
9. Mark Czarnecki, "The Revival of the Creationist Crusade", *MacLean's*, 19 January 1981, p. 56
10. Francis Hitching, *The Neck of the Giraffe: Where Darwin Went Wrong*, New Haven: Tichnor and Fields, 1982, p. 40
11. S. J. Gould, "Evolution's Erratic Pace", *Natural History*, vol. 86, May 1977
12. Peter Douglas Ward, *On Methuselah's Trail*, W. H. Freedman and Company, 1992, p. 10
13. "The Creatures Time Forgot", *New Scientist*, 23 October 1999, p. 36
14. "Balinalarn Evrimi", *National Geographic Turquie*, November 2001, pp. 156-159
15. Niles Eldredge, *Reinventing Darwin*, 1995, p. 77
16. http://www.icr.org/index.php?module=articles&actionview&ID=774
17. Eldredge et Steven M. Stanley. Eds., 1984, Living Fossils, *New York Springer Verlag*, 1984, p. 3
18. Margaret Helder, "Living Fossils: How Significant Are They?", http://www.create.ab.ca/articles/lfossils.html
19. Niles Eldredge, *Reinventing Darwin*, 1995, p. 3
20. Phillip E. Johnson, *Darwin On Trial*, Intervarsity Press, Illinois, 1993, p. 27
21. Jacques Millot, "The Coelacanth", *Scientific American*, vol. 193, December 1955, p. 34
22. Samantha Weinberg, *A Fish Caught in Time: The Search For the Cœlacanth*, Perennial Publishing, 2000, p. 20
23. Ibid., pp. 28-29-30
24. www.ksu.edu/fishecology/relict.htm
25. *Bilim ve Teknik*, Novembre 1998, vol. 372, p. 21 ; http://www. cnn.com/TECH/Science/9809/23/living.fossil/index.html
26. Samantha Weinberg, *A Fish Caught in Time: The Search For the Cœlacanth*, Perennial Publishing, 2000, p. 102
27. P. L. Forey, *Nature*, vol. 336, 1988, p. 7
28. Hans Fricke, "Coelacanths: The Fish That Time Forgot", *National Geographic*, vol. 173, no. 6, June 1988, p. 838
29. *Focus*, April 2003
30. Ibid.
31. Ibid.
32. Ibid.
33. Ibid.
34. Stephen M. Stanley, *Macroevolution: Pattern and Process*, San Francisco: W. H. Freeman and Co. 1979, pp. 35, 159
35. Gould, S. J., 1980, *The Panda's Thumb*, New York: W. W. Norton Co., pp. 186-193
36. http://www.blavatsky.net/features/newsletters/2005/fossil_record.htm
37. Stephen J. Gould, "The Paradox of the First Tier: An Agenda for Paleobiology", *Paleobiology*, 1985, p. 7
38. Niles Eldredge, "Progress in Evolution?", *New Scientist*, vol. 110, 1986, p. 55
39. N. Eldredge et I. Tattersall, *The Myths of Human Evolution*, 1982, p. 48
40. Stephen J. Gould, *"Cordelia's Dilemma"*, *Natural History*, 1993, p. 15
41. Kemp, Tom S., "A Fresh Look at the Fossil Record", *New Scientist*, vol. 108, 1985, pp. 66-67
42. R.A. Fisher, *The Genetical Theory of Natural Selection*, Oxford Univesity Press, 1930
43. Ernst Mayr, Populations, *Species, and Evolution*, Cambridge, Mass: Belknap Press, 1970, p. 235
44. Lane Lester, Raymond Bohlin, *The Natural Limits to Biological Change*, Probe Books, Dallas, 1989, p. 141
45. M. E. Soulé et L. S. Mills, "Enhanced: No Need To Isolate Genetics", *Science*, 1998, vol. 282, p. 165
46. R. L. Westemeier, J. D. Brawn, S. A. Simpson, T. L. Esker, R. W. Jansen, J. W. Walk, E. L. Kershner, J. L. Bouzat et K. N. Paige, "Tracking the Long-term Decline and Recovery of An Isolated Population",
47. Valentine, J., et Erwin, D., *"Interpreting Great Developmental Experiments: The Fossil Record"* in *Development as an Evolutionary Process*, Rudolf A. Raff et Elizabeth C. Raff, Editors, New York: Alan R. Liss, Inc., 1985, p. 96
48. http://www.dhushara.com/book/evol/evop.htm
49. Gould. S. J. et Eldredge. N., 1993, "Punctuated Equilibrium Comes of Age", *Nature*, 366, p. 223
50. R. Dawkins, The Blind Watchmaker, 1986, p. 229.
51. C. Darwin, The Origin of Species, 1st ed., p. 302.
52. M. Czarnecki, McLean's, 19 January 1981, p. 56.
53. H. Gee, In Search of Deep Time, Beyond the Fossil Record to a New History of Life, The Free Press, A Division of Simon & Schuster, Inc.,1999, p. 5.
54. A. S. Romer, Chapter in Genetics, Paleontology and Evolution (1963), p. 114
55. N. Eldredge and I. Tattersall, The Myths of Human Evolution, p. 127.
56. M. Midgley, Evolution as a Religion, London: Routledge Classics, 2002, p. 1.
57. E. O. Wilson, et al., Life on Earth, [1973], Sinauer Associates: Sunderland MA, 1975, reprint, p. 624.
58. F. Hitching, The Neck of the Giraffe: Where Darwin Went Wrong, New York: Ticknor and Fields, 1982, pp. 30-31.
59. F. Hitching, The Neck of the Giraffe, pp. 30-31.

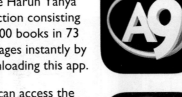

VOLUME - I

English, Turkish, French, German, Italian, Spanish, Russian, Chinese, Japanese, Arabic, Indonesian, Czech, Hindi, Urdu, Bosnian, Swedish

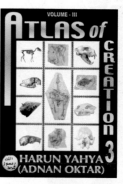

VOLUME - II

English, Turkish, French, German, Spanish, Arabic, Hindi

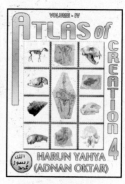

VOLUME - III

English, Turkish, French, German, Spanish, Arabic, Hindi

VOLUME - IV

Turkish, English

English, Turkish, Kyrghyz, Azerbaijani, Danish, Arabic, Bosnian

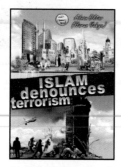

English, Turkish, French, German, Italian, Albanian, Dutch, Azeri, Bengali, Spanish, Russian, Bosnian, Chinese, Arabic, Farsi, Persian, Hausa, Indonesian, Romanian, Swedish

English, Turkish

English, Turkish, French, German, Italian, Spanish, Russian, Chinese, Arabic, Dutch, Czech, Indonesian,, Hindi, Urdu, Bosnian, Polish, Farsi, Hausa, Portuguese, Hebrew, Malay, Serbian, Swedish, Romanian, Hungarian, Danish, Bulgarian, Albenian, Georgian

Turkish - English, Kyrghyz, Hausa

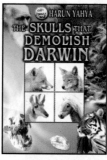

Turkish - English

Turkish - English, German, Kyrghyz

Turkish, English, Kurdi

WISDOM AND SOUND ADVICE FROM THE TORAH

English, Turkish, Hebrew, Azerbaijani

PLEASANT WORDS from the GOSPEL

English, Turkish

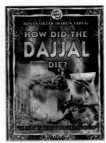

HOW DID THE DAJJAL DIE?

English, Turkish, French, Kyrghyz, Azerbaijani

MAGNICIENT WORLD of the UNDERSEAS

Turkish - English

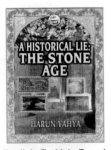

A HISTORICAL LIE: THE STONE AGE

English, Turkish, French, German, Italian, Czech, Malay, Bulgarian, Burmese, Hindi, Urdu, Azerbaijani

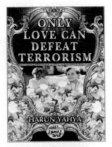

ONLY LOVE CAN DEFEAT TERRORISM

English, Turkish, French, Albanian, Spanish, German, Dutch, Albanian, Indonesian

THE PROPHET MUHAMMAD (saas)

English, Turkish, French, Italian, German, Bosnian, Urdu, Arabic, Azerbaijani, Russian, Malayalam, Danish

THE ORIGINS OF BIRDS AND FLIGHT

English, Turkish

A CALL FOR UNITY

English, Turkish, French, Bulgarian, German

Darwin's Dilemma: The Soul

English, Turkish, Urdu, German, Kyrghyz

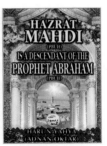

HAZRAT MAHDI (PBUH) IS A DESCENDANT OF THE PROPHET ABRAHAM (PBUH)

English, Turkish, Azerbaijani

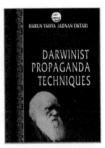

DARWINIST PROPAGANDA TECHNIQUES

English, Turkish, French

IF DARWIN HAD KNOWN ABOUT DNA

English, Turkish, Kyrghyz, Urdu

THE PROPHET JESUS (AS) HAZRAT MAHDI (AS) AND THE ISLAMIC UNION

English, Turkish, Persian

MATTER: THE OTHER NAME FOR ILLUSION

English, Turkish, French, German, Bulgarian, Kyrgyz, Italian, Indonesian, Hindi, Azerbaijani

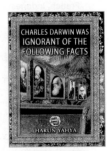

CHARLES DARWIN WAS IGNORANT OF THE FOLLOWING FACTS

English, Turkish

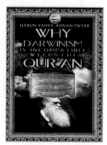

**WHY DARWINISM IS INCOMPATIBLE WITH THE QUR'AN**

English, Turkish, French, German, Arabic, Indonesian

**THE QUR'AN LEADS THE WAY TO SCIENCE**

English, Turkish, French, German, Albanian, Azeri, Spanish, Russian, Indonesian, Urdu

**A CALL FOR A TURKISH-ISLAMIC UNION**

English, Turkish, French, Albanian, Urdu, German, Kyrghyz

**THE INTELLECTUAL STRUGGLE AGAINST DARWINISM**

English, Turkish, French, German, Kyrgyz

**DARK SPELL OF DARWINISM**

English, Turkish

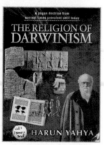

**THE RELIGION OF DARWINISM**

English, Turkish, French, German, Indonesian

**THE TRANSITIONAL FORM DILEMMA**

English, Turkish, Italian

**ONCE UPON A TIME THERE WAS DARWINISM**

English, Turkish, French, German, Italian, Spanish, Arabic

**Tell Me About CREATION**

English, Turkish, German, Italian, French, Indonesian

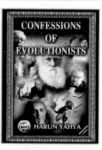

**CONFESSIONS OF EVOLUTIONISTS**

English, Turkish

**A DEFINITIVE REPLY TO EVOLUTIONIST PROPAGANDA**

English, Turkish

**FACTS THAT DARWINISTS DON'T WANT TO RECOGNIZE**

English, Turkish

**THE NATURE OF THE DARWINIST IMPASSE**

English, Turkish, German, Italian, Indonesian

**ETERNITY HAS ALREADY BEGUN**

English, Turkish, French, Albanian, Azerbaijani, Spanish, Russian, Urdu, Malay, Arabic, Kyrgyz

**THE RESPONSES EXPECTED BY DARWINISTS**

English, Turkish

**DARWIN'S MISGUIDED SUCCESSORS**

English, Turkish

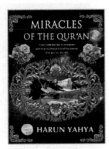

English, Turkish, French, German, Polish, Albanian, Dutch, Azeri, Bengali, Spanish, Russian, Bosnian, Arabic, Farsi, Indonesian, Urdu, Polish, Uzbek, Tamil, Pashto, Thai, Greek, Malay

English, Turkish, French, German, Hebrew

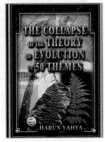
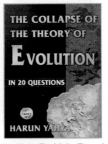

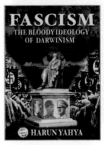

English, Turkish, Czech

English, Turkish, French, German, Azerbaijani, Spanish, Arabic, Indonesian

English, Turkish, French, German, Italian, Japanese, Indonesian, Azerbaijani

English, Turkish, German, Indonesian

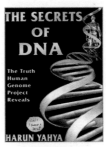
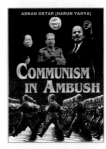

English, Turkish

English, Turkish

English, Turkish

English, Turkish, Bosnian, Burmese, French

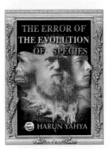
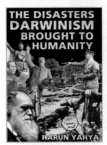

English, Turkish, French, German, Azeri, Spanish, Italian, Danish, Azerbaijani, Kyrghyz

English, Turkish

English, Turkish, German

English, Turkish, French, German, Albanian, Bengali, Spanish, Arabic, Burmese, Indonesian, Serbian, Malay

English, Turkish,
German

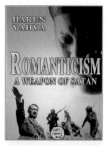

English, Turkish, French,
Azeri, Arabic, Indonesian

English, Turkish,
German, Indonesian

English, Turkish,
Malay

English, Turkish,
German, Bengali,
Indonesian, Azerbaijani,
Bulgarian, Kiswahili

English, Turkish,
Indonesian,
Azerbaijani

English, Turkish,
French, Malayalam

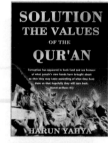

English,Turkish,
French, Italian, Arabic,
Bengali, Albanian

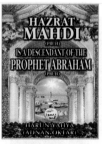

English,Turkish,
Azerbaijani

English, Turkish

English, Turkish,
German, Czech

English, Turkish, Azeri, Ur
Malay, Persian, Indonesia

English, Bosnian

English, Turkish, German,
Indonesian, Czech

English, Turkish, Arabic,
Indonesian, Bosnian

English, Turkish,
Russian, Kyrghyz

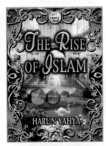

**English, Turkish, Albanian**

**Turkish**

**English, Turkish, Bulgarian**

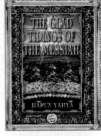

**English, Turkish, French**

**English, Turkish, French, German, Albanian, Urdu, Arabic, Kyrgyz, Azerbaijani**

**English, Turkish, French, German, Albanian, Bengali, Spanish, Arabic, Indonesian, Tatar, Kyrghyz**

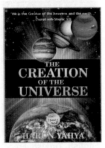

**English, Turkish, French, German, Italian, Albanian, Chinese, Spanish, Russian, Arabic, Indonesian, Urdu**

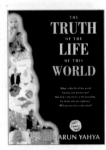

**English, Turkish, French, German, Italian, Albanian, Chinese, Czech, Spanish, Russian, Arabic, Urdu Indonesian, Azerbaijani, Hungarian**

**English, Turkish, French, Dutch, Arabic**

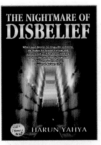

**English, Turkish, French, Czech, Arabic**

**English, Turkish, French, Urdu, Albanian, Azerbaijani, Georgian, Russian, Romanian**

**English, Turkish, French, Albanian, Azerbaijani, German, Bosnian**

**English, Turkish, Azerbaijani**

**English, Turkish, Italian, Arabic, Bosnian, Azerbaijani**

**English, Turkish, French, Azerbaijani, German, Bulgarian, Bengali**

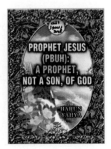

**English, Turkish, French, Bulgarian**

English, Turkish,
Azerbaijani, Indonesian

English, Turkish,
Hungarian, Azerbaijani,
Kyrghyz

English, Turkish,
Pashto

English, Turkish,
Albanian, German,
Persian, Kyrghyz

English, Turkish,
Chinese, Arabic,
Indonesian,
Azerbaijani

English, Turkish, French,
German, Italian, Albanian,
Dutch, Azerbaijani,
Pashto, Spanish, Russian,
Bengali, Chinese, Arabic,
Persian, Urdu,
Indonesian, Portuguese,
Bulgarian

English, Turkish

English, Turkish,
French, German,
Urdu

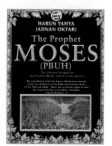

English, Turkish, French,
Albanian, Azerbaijani,
German, Bosnian, Arabic

English, Turkish

English, Turkish,
Arabic

English, Turkish,
Persian

English, Turkish,
Azerbaijani, German,
Bosnian

English, Turkish,
German

English, Turkish,
German

English, Turkish,
Indonesian, Malayalam

English, Turkish,
German, Arabic,
Kyrghyz

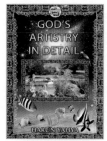

English, Turkish,
Persian, Azerbaijani,
Urdu

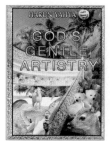

English, Turkish,
German

English, Turkish,
French, Kyrgyz

English, Turkish, French,
German, Kyrgyz, Arabic,
Spanish

English, Turkish, French,
German, Albanian, Arabic,
Burmese, Indonesian,
Persian, Urdu, Italian,
Spanish, Azerbaijani

English, Turkish, French,
German, Albanian, Arabic,
Bengali, Indonesian

English, Turkish, French,
German, Azerbaijani,
Urdu, Russian,
Indonesian, Arabic

English, Turkish,
Azerbaijani, Kyrghyz

English, Turkish,
French

English, Turkish,
German

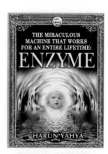

English, Turkish,
Urdu, Azerbaijan,

English, Turkish

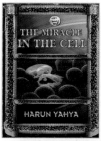

English, Turkish,
Kyrghyz

English, Turkish,
Arabic, Kyrghyz

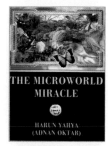

English, Turkish

English, Turkish,
German, Kyrghyz

English, Turkish,
Indonesian

English, Turkish,
French, Arabic, Kyrghyz

English, Turkish,
German

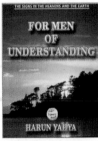

English, Turkish, French,
German, Italian, Danish,
Urdu, Spanish, Russian,
Serbian, Persian,
Indonesian

English, Turkish,
French, German, Italian,
Spanish, Russian,
Indonesian, Arabic

English, Turkish,
French, German, Urdu,
Azerbaijani, Albanian,
Indonesian, Arabic

English, Turkish, French,
Azerbaijani, Swahili,
Spanish, Arabic, Persian,
Indonesian, Serbian,
Macedonian

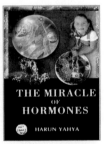

English, Turkish,
Arabic, Indonesian

English, Turkish, French,
German, Kyrgyz, Persian,
Swidish,

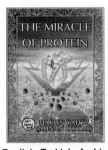

English, Turkish, Arabic,
Azerbaijani, Kyrghyz

English, Turkish,
Kyyghyz

English, Turkish

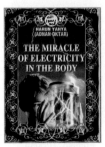

English, German,
Kyrghyz, Urdu

English, Turkish,
German

English, Turkish,
German

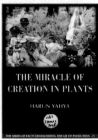
THE MIRACLE OF
CREATION IN PLANTS

English, Turkish,
French, Arabic,
German, Serbian

SIGNS FROM THE QUR'AN

English, Turkish,
Urdu

THE CAMBRIAN

English, Turkish

THE MIRACLES
OF SMELL AND
TASTE

English, Turkish,
German, Arabic

THE MIRACLE
IN THE
SPIDER

English, Turkish,
French, Urdu,
Indonesian, Arabic

A CHAIN OF MIRACLES

English, Turkish, Persian,
German, Hungarian,
Indonesian, Arabic

ALLAH'S
ARTISTRY
IN COLOUR

English, Turkish, German,
Urdu, Albanian, Bosnian,
Indonesian, Arabic

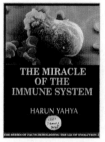
THE MIRACLE
OF THE
IMMUNE SYSTEM

English, Turkish, French,
Serbian, Albanian, Kyrghyz,
Indonesian, Arabic

THE MIRACLE
IN THE SEED

English, Turkish,
German

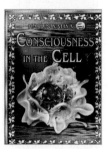
CONSCIOUSNESS
IN THE CELL

English, Turkish,
Arabic, Albanian

GLOBAL
FREEMASONRY

English, Turkish, French, German,
Albanian, Azerbaijani, Swedish,
Burmese, Swahili, Indonesian

WHAT
DARWINISTS
FAIL TO CONSIDER

English, Turkish,
Urdu, Chinese

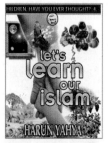
MIRACLE
IN THE EYE

English, Turkish,
German, Kyrghyz

let's learn our islam

English, Turkish, French,
German, Albanian, Spanish,
Polish, Malay, Arabic,
Indonesian, Urdu, Arabic,
Bosnian, Russian, Urdu

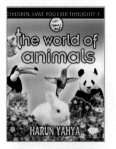
the world of animals

English, Turkish, French,
German, Spanish, Polish,
Persian, Arabic, Indonesian,
Bosnian, Russian

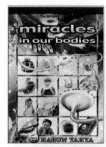
miracles
in our bodies

English, Turkish, French,
German, Azerbaijani, Urdu,
Albanian, Arabic,
Indonesian, Bosnian

English, Turkish, French, German, Spanish, Arabic, Urdu, Indonesian, Serbian, Bosnian, Portuguese, Malay

English, Turkish, French, Persian, Arabic, Malay Indonesian, Swahili, Bosnian, Russian

English, Turkish, French, German, Uzbek, Albanian, Dutch, Azerbaijani, Amharic, Spanish, Bosnian, Arabic, Persian, Indonesian

English, Turkish, German

English, Turkish, French, Norwegian, Albanian, Dutch, Azeri, Czech, Spanish, Arabic, Farsi, Indonesian, Russian

English, Turkish, French, Albanian, Arabic, Urdu, Indonesian, Azerbaijani

English, Spanish, Albanian, Turkish

English, Turkish, French, German, Dutch, Danish, Persian, Russian, Arabic, Indonesian, Thai, Bosnian, Portuguese, Malay

English, Turkish, German

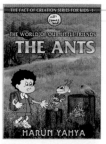

English, Turkish, French, German, Thai, Dutch, Albanian, Bengali,Spanish, Russian, Bosnian, Malay, Danish, Arabic, Persian, Indonesian, Portuguese, Urdu, Chinese

English, Turkish, German, Russian, Malayalam, Bosnian, Malay, Arabic, Indonesian, Persian

English,Turkish, German, French

English, Albanian, Turkish, Spanish, German, French, Hungarian, Azebaijani, Dutch

English, Albanian, Spanish, Turkish, Russian

English, Persian, Turkish, Spanish, Albanian, Italian, French, German, Dutch, Arabic

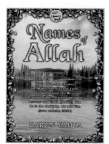

English, Turkish,
French, Russian

English, Turkish,
Arabic, Indonesian

English, German,
Turkish, Italian, Urdu

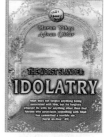

English, Russian,
Turkish, Arabic

English, Turkish,
Albanian, Maranao,
Frrench, German,
Russian

English, Turkish,
Bengali, Czech,
Indonesian,
French

English, Turkish,
French, Polish, Spanish,
Urdu, Hungarian,
Bulgarian

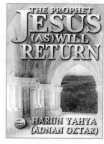

English, German,
Portuguese, Bosnian,
Arabic, Bulgarian,
Indonesian, Turkish,
French, Bengali,
Russian, Italian, Albanian

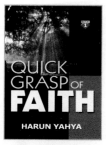

English, Turkish, Arabic,
German, Indonesian,
Russian, French,

English, Turkish,
German

English, Turkish,
German

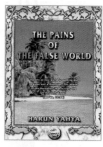

English, Hungarian,
Turkish

English, Turkish,
Almanca

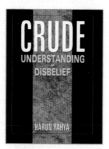

English, German,
Indonesian, Albanian,
Turkish

English, French,
Indonesian, Arabic, Italian,
Turkish, German, Albanian

English, Albanian, Kyrgyz,
French, Turkish, Burmese,
Hungarian, German

# HARUN YAHYA DOCUMENTARIES
# ON DVD & VCD

## 40 Pcs. DVDs Documentary Film Set

40 DVD set with WorldWide FREE SHIPPING

New

[DVDs]:

1- The Creation of the Universe
2- The Secret Beyond Matter
3- Miracles of the Qur'an
4- The Miracle of Man's Creation
5- Perished Nations -I
6- Allah's Artistry in Color
7- Islam Denounces Terrorism
8- The Qur'an Leads the Way to Science
9- The Signs of the Last Day
10- The Truth of the Life of This World
11- The Secret of the Test
12- The Bloody History of Communism I
13- The Bloody History of Communism II
14- The Fact of Creation
15- The Miracle in the Ant
16- The End Times and the Mahdi
17- Love and Cooperation in Living Things
18- The Miracle Planet - I
19- Splendour in the Seas
20- Perished Nations -II

21- Allah is Known Through Reason
22- Deep Thinking
23- For Men of Understanding –I
24- For Men of Understanding -II
25- For Men of Understanding -III
26- Miracles of the Brain : Smell and Taste
27- The Miracle in the Cell
28- Behind the Scenes of the World Wars
29- Answers from the Qur'an
30- The Collapse of the Theory of Evolution
31- The Collapse of Atheism
32- The Disasters Darwinism Brought to Humanity
33- Altruism in Nature
34- The Miracle of Seed
35- Biomimetics: Technology Imitates Nature
36- The Names of Allah
37- Satanism: Satan's Bloody Teaching
38- The Miracle of Respiration
39- Solution: The Values of the Qur'an
40- The Miracle Planet II

## 10 Pcs. DVDs
## Multi Language DVD Set

1- The Signs of The Last Day
2- The Truth of the Life of This World
3- Allah Is Known Through Reason
4- Deep Thinking
5- Allah's Artistry In Color
6- The Fact of Creation
7- For Men of Understanding-I
8- For Men of Understanding-II
9- For Men of Understanding-III
10- Love and Cooperation in Living Things

## 20 Pcs. VCDs

### For Men of Understanding Documentary Series VCDs

VCD1: The End Times and Mahdi
       Technology in Nature
VCD2: The Miracle of Seed
       Miracles of the Brain:Smell and Taste
VCD3: Perished Nations-I
       Perished Nations-II
VCD4: The Truth of the Life of This World
       Solution: The Values of the Qur'an
VCD5: Architects in Nature
       Allah Is Known Through Reason
VCD6: Allah's Artistry in Color
       Love and Cooperation in Living Things
VCD7: The Creation of the Universe
       The Miracle Planet
VCD8: Behind the Scenes of the World Wars
       The Miracle of Respiration
VCD9: Signs of the Last Day
       The Miracle in the Ant
VCD10: The Miracle in the Cell
        Deep Thinking

# SOME WEB SITES WHERE YOU CAN ACCESS THE WORKS OF HARUN YAHYA

www.harunyahya.com
www.harunyahyainternationalmedia.com
www.darkdangerbigotry.com
www.solutiontopkk.com
www.king-messiah.com
www.primepeace.com
www.adnanoktarsays.com
www.harunyahyasays.com
www.redemptionofjews.com
www.evolutioninternational.net
www.religionofdarwinism.com
www.darwinismthegreatestlieinhistory.com
www.creationofman.net
www.dnarefutesevolution.com
www.theprophetjesus.com
www.mahdineversheddsblood.com
www.muslimspersecuted.com
www.islamandkarma.com
www.eastturkestan.com
www.signsofthelastday.com
www.sheikhnazimalhaqqani.com
www.darwinistsneverrealize.com
www.adnanoktarinterviews.com
www.dailycomments.net
www.primepeace.com
www.skullsdemolishdarwinism.com
www.returningtofaith.com
www.thestoneage.org
www.dayofjudgment.com
www.truthsforkids.com
www.womaninthequran.com
www.islamandbuddhism.com
www.servingislam.com
www.palestiniantragedy.com
www.theislamicunion.com
www.darwinism-watch.com
www.scienceresearchfoundation.com
www.evolutiontale.com
www.evolutionisnotscientific.com
www.mythofhomology.com
www.darwinistsdilemma.com
www.realityofdeath.com
www.harunyahyaconferences.com
www.whydarwinwaswrong.com
www.darksideofdarwinism.com
www.romanticismaweaponofsatan.com
www.darwinistcorruptioninthearabworld.com
www.bird-fossils.com
www.commentsonatlasofcreation.com
www.realityofdeath.com

www.mahdiaccordingtofoursunnischools.com
www.wisdomfromtorah.com
www.miracleoflightandcolour.com
www.reptile-fossils.com
www.mahdiaccordingtoholyscriptures.com
www.hereafterexists.com
www.formanunderstanding.com
www.quranindex.net
www.humanisamiracle.com
www.miracleintheeye.com
www.miracleinthespider.com
www.miracleofthebloodandheart.com
www.miracleintheatom.com
www.darwinismssocialweapon.com
www.mahdiaccordingtofoursunnischools.com
www.fascismandcommunism.com
www.byvirtueofharunyahya.com
www.whydarwinwaswrong.com
www.for-children.com
www.Allahexists.com
www.freeislamicbooks.net
www.worldwarsunveiled.com
www.cambriananddarwin.com
www.bbcrefuted.com
www.harunyahyasays.com
www.riseofislam.com
www.falseworld.net
www.darwinisminruins.com
www.naturalselectionanddarwinism.com
www.mythofhomology.com
www.oldestmushroom.com
www.harunyahyaimpact.com
www.nationalacademyofsciencesrefuted.com
www.divxvar.com
www.darwinistsinmourning.com
www.darwinismisso19thcentury.com
www.grievingdarwinists.com
www.darwinistsdefeated.com
www.darwinistsinpain.com
www.ambersdenydarwin.com
www.whatdarwindidnotknow.com
www.darwinslostcause.com
www.insight-magazine.com
www.brothercountry-iran.com
www.adnanoktar.us
www.miracleofhormones.com
www.natureandbiomimetics.com
www.englishkuran.com
www.psychologicalwarfaremethods.com
www.nocompulsioninislam.com

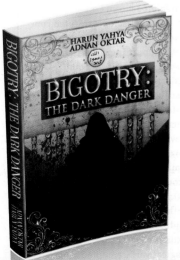

ADNAN OKTAR (HARUN YAHYA)'S LATEST BOOK:

# BIGOTRY: THE DARK DANGER

This book is hugely important because it describes things you have never heard before about Islam and sets out the true reason for the radical terror currently plaguing the world.

This book explains why a terrorist will kill someone in the name of Islam, sets out why there are such intense efforts in the name of Islam to exclude women from the outside world and clarifies the toxic and dangerous ideological perspective that maintains the need for "enmity" toward almost every community in the name of Islam. And it reveals a most important truth; this toxic mindset does not belong to Islam at all. Islam lies in the Qur'an, not in superstitions, or in various fabricated hadiths or consensus of scholars: The

religion described in the Qur'an demands love, democracy, quality, joy and peace. This fact, known to few people in the world, is set out in this book. It describes the false faith and sinister world of the fanatics from their own source materials, while defining the true Islam with explicit evidence from the Qur'an. The book is an excellent resource for anyone seeking a solution to radical terror, hostility to democracy, the lack of quality and the seemingly interminable rage we see in so many corners of the world in the name of Islam. The only solution to a damaging concept of religion based on superstition is to eliminate that superstition through the truth. The solution lies in this book.